'Did. . .did yo
last night?'

Ross shrugged. 'Yes,

'But I made it quite clear that I wasn't prepared to share a bedroom with you!' she
retorted angrily. 'Any man with an *ounce* of
sensibility and tact——'

'Oh, come on, Laura! Even if I were a man of
sensibility and tact, I still needed a good night's
sleep. And besides,' he added, 'you seemed
remarkably content in my arms last night!'

WE HOPE you're enjoying our new addition to our Contemporary Romance series—stories which take a light-hearted look at the Zodiac and show that love can be written in the stars!

Every month you can get to know a different combination of star-crossed lovers, with one story that follows the fortunes of a hero or a heroine when they embark on the romance of a lifetime. This month features a sizzling love-affair between two **LEOs**.

To find out more fascinating facts about this month's featured star sign, turn to the back pages of this book. . .

ABOUT THIS MONTH'S AUTHOR

Mary Lyons says: 'In many ways I am a typical Gemini. As my husband says, I must have been born with a phone in my hand, and my nose in a book. He also maintains that I'm a mine of useless information.

'He may be right about my love of reading. I've always been a fan of romantic fiction, and nowadays I can hardly believe my luck at having all the fun and satisfaction involved in writing romances for others to read.'

DOUBLE FIRE

BY

MARY LYONS

MILLS & BOON LIMITED
ETON HOUSE   18–24 PARADISE ROAD
RICHMOND   SURREY   TW9 1SR

First published in Great Britain 1992
by Mills & Boon Limited

© Mary Lyons 1992

Australian copyright 1992
Philippine copyright 1992
This edition 1992

ISBN 0 263 77613 1

STARSIGN ROMANCES is a trademark of Harlequin Enterprises B.V., Fribourg Branch. Mills and Boon is an authorised user.

Set in 10 on 12 pt Linotron Baskerville
01-9207-52577 Z

Typeset in Great Britain by Centracet, Cambridge
Made and printed in Great Britain

CHAPTER ONE

'WELL . . .? Did you enjoy the party? And was it *really* a surprise?'

Laura Wyndham's deep sapphire-blue eyes sparkled with amusement, her lips widening into a broad, wry smile as she entered the large living-room of the penthouse apartment.

'The answer to both your questions is yes,' she told the girl sitting at a long table on the far side of the room. 'Although I must say, Julie,' she added, throwing her briefcase down on to a nearby chair, 'I do think that you might have given me the "Gypsy's Warning" before I left for work today!'

'Ah, but then it wouldn't have been a surprise, would it?' Julie pointed out with devastating logic as she corrected the last of the school-books piled up on the large oak refectory table in front of her. Smiling across the room at Laura's tall, slender figure, she added, 'Besides, everyone in your office was so pleased at your promotion. It isn't every day that someone starts on the ground floor and ends up by being made a director of the firm. Your colleagues had gone to so much trouble to organise the party. I'd have hated to have spoiled their fun.'

'Yes, well. . . I must admit that it *was* fun,' Laura agreed. Shrugging off the severely cut navy blue linen jacket of her new designer suit, she tossed it over on top

5

of her briefcase, before sinking down on to a sofa and sighing with relief as she slipped off her high-heeled blue court shoes.

'You sound tired.'

'Hmm. . .yes, I am.' Laura yawned as she leaned back against the cushions. 'Quite apart from the party in the wine bar this evening, it's been a very hectic day in the office. Wall Street seemed to go completely mad this afternoon!' She stifled another yawn. 'And I can't say I'm looking forward to tomorrow, either. Some female reporter from *Business Finance Magazine* is supposed to be spending the morning with me. She's apparently writing an article about "Successful Women in the City".'

'Wow. . .fame at last!' Julie laughed.

'Ha-ha!' Laura pulled a face. 'In fact, if we're busy at work I can see that having to try and explain all the complexities of the London Metal Exchange to someone who knows absolutely nothing about it is going to be a *real* drag.' She shrugged her shoulders. 'However, that's enough about me. How were all your little darlings. . .?'

Julie, who taught at a local school in a notoriously rough, tough area of the city, shrugged her shoulders. 'The kids were fairly quiet today, thank goodness. But, let's face it, most of the twelve-year-olds that I teach seem to know nothing about mathematics—and care even less!'

'I wish I could go back to being twelve again,' Laura muttered gloomily. 'I certainly didn't need my boss, Tim Dunton, informing me that when I reach the ripe old age of twenty-six, in just over a month's time, it's going to be definitely downhill all the way!'

'Oh, dear—you poor old hag!' her friend murmured

sardonically, grinning as she deftly caught hold of the cushion Laura had sent flying across the room towards her. 'Anyway, you know that Tim is only saying that because he wants you to marry him. Right?'

'Well. . .yes, I suppose so.'

'By the way, have you told him that you haven't yet got a divorce? That you are, in fact, still married to Ross?'

Laura's cheeks flushed. 'Umm. . .not exactly. I mean——'

'Oh, Laura—you really *are* hopeless!' Julie exclaimed, shaking her head as she gazed across the room at her old friend's straight shoulder-length rich golden hair, brushed back from her forehead like a lion's mane, and shimmering in the soft glow from the lamp on the table beside her. 'How can you look a million dollars, be so terrifically successful in business—and yet your personal life seem to be in such a mess?'

Laura gave a heavy sigh. It was no wonder that Julie clearly thought she ought to have her head examined. And it probably was stupid—if not downright ridiculous—for her to be *still* technically married to a man she hadn't seen for almost five years. However, now that the papers had been reporting the recent news of her husband's return from Australia—apparently determined to impress his name and tough personality on the City of London—it was obviously about time that she came to a decision about her future.

'Wyndham' wasn't a very unusual name and, so far, no one seemed to suspect that she had any connection with the newsworthy, hard and formidable entrepreneur Ross Wyndham. Over the last few months hardly a day had gone by without his name being mentioned in the financial Press, the articles mainly commenting on the swift, ferocious manner in which he was carving his way through the City, ruthlessly gobbling up one company after another.

However, if she couldn't make up her mind what to do about divorcing Ross. . . Laura was quite sure that she didn't want to marry her boss, Tim Dunton. She was very fond of him, of course, but she knew that she didn't love him. Although, since she'd once experienced the so-called 'real thing'—a wild, tempestuous tide of overwhelming emotion and desire, which had brought her nothing but misery and unhappiness—well, maybe there *was* something to be said for a warm, calm and friendly relationship. . .?

'I'll admit that—er—I do seem to need to get a few minor items in my life sorted out,' Laura told her friend nonchalantly.

'"A few *minor* items". . .? Who are you kidding?' Julie gave a hoot of laughter. 'Honestly, Laura—you're such a typical Leo woman, it just isn't true!'

'Oh, for heaven's sake! You're not still going on about all that star sign nonsense, are you? I can't think why you bother with that rubbish,' Laura added dismissively.

'It's *not* rubbish,' her friend protested. 'Even when we were at school together, you used to lord it over the rest of us, and would *never* admit that you were capable of making any mistakes. And who could ever forget the row you kicked up the one year you weren't chosen to play Mary in the school nativity play?' Julie added with a rueful laugh.

'Yes, well. . .that was all a long time ago,' Laura said

firmly. 'And, anyway, I have got some good qualities, haven't I?'

Julie grinned. 'Of course you have, you idiot! Apart from being beautiful and elegant, not to mention clever and intelligent—you've one of the kindest hearts I know. Will that do to go on with?' she added, smiling to herself. Despite what she might say, Laura—who was *definitely* a typical Leo lady—clearly appreciated hearing her virtues praised. And why not? Julie told herself. Because it was certainly true that Laura Wyndham had been incredibly kind and generous to her, and to many of their less fortunate friends. It was just a tragedy that her friend had married a man whose birthday came under the same sign as her own. She'd only met him a few times, but it had been easy for Julie to see that Ross Wyndham was even more Leo-like than his wife. And the fiery explosion which had resulted from two large egos clashing had blown their marriage to smithereens.

'The fact that, after five years of separation, I'm still married to Ross is nothing more than a *mere* technicality!' Laura told the other girl, ignoring her bark of sardonic laughter. 'And, if I haven't yet got around to getting a divorce, it's. . .well, it's just because I've been working so hard, that's all.'

'*Oh, sure*. . .!' Julie murmured in a sceptical tone of voice as she rose from the table. 'It's late, and about time that I went to bed. But, just before I do, I hope you'll remember that it's *me* you're talking to—the old school-friend who's known you since the year dot. OK. . .?'

'OK—OK!' Laura gave her a sheepish grin.

'And, talking of old school-friends,' Julie said, pausing

in the doorway of her bedroom, 'your cousin Liz tele-
phoned from New York to say hello, and she was
delighted to hear about your new position in the firm.'

'It was sweet of her to ring—I'm sorry I missed her.'
Laura's lips curved into a warm smile at the thought of
her cousin, the girl with whom she'd grown up, and
whom she loved as dearly as a sister.

'Apparently, Owen is intending to take Liz off for a
weekend trip, all on their own, while the children are
going to stay with a friend. It's the Independence Day
celebrations in the United States next Monday, and,
from what Liz said, it seems that most people in America
are making it a long holiday weekend.'

'That sounds a good idea. I know that Liz could do
with a break. Even though they're now five years old, I
gather that the twins are still quite a handful.'

'I can believe it!' Julie laughed before saying good-
night and closing her bedroom door.

Knowing that she had a long day in front of her,
Laura decided to follow her friend's good example.
Unfortunately, over one hour later she found herself
lying back against the pillows and staring up at the
ceiling, completely unable to go to sleep. It was some
time before she realised that she wasn't just wide
awake—she was hungry! Thanks to working late in the
office, followed by the celebrations on her becoming a
director of her firm, she had somehow omitted to have
anything to eat. And without filling the giant-sized hole
in her stomach there was no way she was going to be
able to go off to sleep.

Slipping on a light cotton robe, she padded across the
thick bedroom carpet, through the large living-room and

into the kitchen. Only having moved into this new warehouse apartment just over two months ago, Laura still wasn't quite sure how most of the ultra-modern appliances actually worked. Maybe if she and Julie didn't have such tiring, exhausting jobs they might have more time to concentrate on the culinary arts. As it was, the only items in this futuristic, state-of-the-art kitchen with which she was totally familiar were the microwave oven, the toaster and the electric kettle. What an indictment on her way of life!

With a wry shrug of her slim shoulders Laura made herself a ham sandwich before wandering back into what the estate agent's particulars had referred to as 'a huge reception-room'. She didn't have either the time or the inclination to hold 'receptions'—whatever they might be—but when she returned home at night, exhausted from her day in the City, she never failed to appreciate the deep sense of peaceful calm and serenity of the large, thickly carpeted room. Her job might be one of considerable stress and strain, but she really had been incredibly lucky, Laura told herself, not just in being able to afford to buy a penthouse apartment in this large, architectually prestigious warehouse development beside the river at Wapping, but also in managing to persuade her old school-friend Julie to come and share the apartment with her.

Julie hadn't a bean, of course, but that didn't matter. In fact, Laura had refused to accept from her friend anything more than a small token sum towards the other girl's rent. Because, with the death of her father just over a year ago, and with her only other living relative, her cousin Liz, living so far away in America, both she and

Julie—who also had no close family of her own—were able to provide company for each other.

Making herself a cup of hot chocolate, Laura carried it out on to the small balcony overlooking the dark green water of the River Thames. Although there had been a light summer shower earlier in the evening, it was now a warm, clear night with just a soft breeze rustling the ropes and canvas of the small boats berthed in the marina far below.

It was a pity that she'd missed her cousin's phone call. However, she was pleased that Liz's husband, Owen Wyndham—despite being a perfect example of an absent-minded professor—had obviously realised his wife needed a short holiday.

Laura smiled to herself as she thought about her scatty cousin and her husband, who never seemed to have his feet on the ground either. However, there was no doubt that, despite Owen's low salary as a lecturer in philosophy at Columbia University, and the fact that they had two small children to clothe and feed, her cousin and her husband were amazingly happy and contented together.

Laura was due to go over and stay with them in September. But goodness knows where she was going to sleep. The small apartment on Riverside Drive sounded as though it was already full to overflowing. However, Liz had laughed like a drain when she had commented on how small it sounded.

'Small. . .? Hah! Honestly, Laura, you've absolutely *no* idea just how expensive property is here in New York. *You* might earn almost a quarter of a million pounds a year——'

'Hey—it's not quite as much as that!'

'—but if Ross hadn't twisted Owen's arm and made him take the money we wouldn't have been able to afford even a shoe-box. I know that you don't like me talking about Ross,' she'd added apologetically, 'but he really has been very kind and generous.'

Ross. . .! Laura squirmed uncomfortably in her chair. If there was one person she *really* didn't want to think about it was Owen's elder brother—and the man who was also her own husband—Ross Wyndham.

The fact that she and Liz had married two brothers was something that was much more likely to happen in fiction than in real life. Unfortunately there was nothing fictitious about the situation in which she now found herself—and one which she really must resolve as soon as possible.

When Liz's parents had both been tragically killed in an air crash over Paris Liz—an eleven-year-old orphan—had come to live with Laura and her parents in the old stone manor house, part of a large estate which had been in the Harding family for generations.

Helen Harding, the sister of Liz's mother, and her husband James Harding, the senior partner in a large firm of lawyers in Plymouth, had provided a loving home for their young niece. And they had always treated Liz— the same age as Laura—just as though she were their own child.

Laura grinned as she recalled her early teens when she and Liz, together with their school-friend Julie, had spent the holidays climbing trees, swimming, and bicycling around the beautiful Devonshire countryside.

Even at school, Liz had always been a very gifted

painter. And, despite being fairly scatty and not particularly intellectual, she'd worked very hard to gain the
necessary qualifications which would enable her to
attend an art college in London. There, her bright and
bubbly personality had ensured that she was one of the
most popular girls in her year.

Laura, a far more quiet and serious character than
her cousin, had left home at the same time for
Cambridge University, to read economics. Finding
themselves studying such very different subjects, and
with each of them making a circle of new friends—none
of whom had anything in common with the other's
friends—it was no wonder that Laura and Liz had
begun to drift slowly apart. In fact, it was only on Liz's
engagement and marriage to Owen Wyndham, a young
lecturer in philosophy at London University, that they'd
become close friends once more.

That wedding between Liz and Owen had proved to
be a watershed in all their lives. It was the last public
appearance of Laura's mother, Helen, who very soon
after had suddenly collapsed and died from a completely
unsuspected kidney complaint. And it was at the wedding of her cousin that Laura had first met Owen's older
brother, Ross Wyndham.

Laura had often wondered whether their union had
always been doomed to failure. . .whether her deep
unhappiness at the sudden death of her mother, and her
father's disastrous illness, had merely accelerated the
inevitable swift decline and end to her marriage.

Alzheimer's Disease was now widely known and
recognised as an incurable form of senile dementia. But,
in those early days of her marriage, her father had

merely seemed to be a deeply unhappy if somewhat eccentric man, whose small losses of memory were hardly noticeable. And even those could be put down to excessive grief at the loss of his wife. However, only six months after her wedding to Ross, Laura had become increasingly disturbed by her father's odd behaviour. Even his colleagues had been alarmed by James Harding's confused state of mind, and had persuaded him to seek medical help.

Laura had been shattered by the swift deterioration in her father's mental health, and to hear the official diagnosis from their family doctor. And, on a quick trip down to Devon, it had been a considerable shock to discover the full extent of the problem. Quite apart from her father's permanent state of confusion and memory disorder, it seemed that he had also been possibly guilty of embezzlement. Large sums of money were missing from the business, and while his colleagues now realised that her father was ill—and obviously hadn't deliberately intended to commit any kind of fraud—nevertheless, the money had had to be replaced as quickly as possible.

There had been only one obvious course of action— and that had been to raise the necessary sums by selling the family estate.

However, it was while in the midst of dealing with her father's problems that her husband had dropped his bombshell. Ross, who'd taken over the industrial empire founded by his father, Sir David Wyndham, had been planning to develop and broaden the company's overseas operations. And, with that end in view, Ross had made arrangements for their immediate departure for Australia.

It had all seemed too much for Laura to cope with. On the one hand, she knew that, with Liz living abroad, she was the only person capable of coping with her father's problems. And yet, on the other hand, her husband was insisting that her loyalties must lie with him—and their new life on the far side of the world.

Practically torn apart by conflicting loyalties—and with Ross refusing to accept the idea that she might, somehow, be able to divide her life between the two continents—Laura hadn't known what to do. However, in the end it had seemed as though Ross had made the decision for her. Issuing an imperative ultimatum, which had given her no room for manoeuvre, and with which he must have known she couldn't possibly have agreed, he had abruptly and swiftly left the country.

Laura had been given no time to mourn the collapse of her brief marriage. She had been far too busy trying to cope with the sale of the large estate, and by the time all her father's debts had been settled there had been nothing left except the old Elizabethan Manor House.

'I'm afraid that you still have a major problem,' the family lawyer had pointed out. 'As you know, your father now needs constant twenty-four-hour medical care, and nursing homes specialising in the treatment of his disease can be very expensive. If, maybe, your cousin could help financially as well. . .?'

'No—I don't want her to be dragged into this mess,' Laura had told him firmly. 'Not only is she living thousands of miles away, in New York, but she's also expecting twins any day now! Besides. . .' Laura had shrugged '. . . Liz and her husband are as poor as church mice. So I reckon that it's up to me to get a job and pay for Dad's medical care.'

The lawyer had given a gloomy shake of his head. And when she'd learned the full amount of the financial sums involved Laura hadn't felt too cheerful either. However, with youthful if foolish optimism she had proudly assured him that she would find a solution to the problem. And amazingly, against all the odds, she had succeeded in doing so.

When Liz's twin baby girls were born Laura was convinced that she had done the right thing in keeping the full extent of her father's illness and the subsequent disastrous financial mess from her cousin. Even when Liz had come over for Mr Harding's funeral, which had taken place just over a year ago, Laura hadn't felt able to explain all of the difficulties she had faced. And she certainly had never confessed to the family pressures that lay behind the break-up of her marriage.

'I'm so glad that Uncle James didn't sell the family home,' Liz had said as they had walked around the garden just before she had left Devon to catch the plane back to New York. 'And how lucky that he left enough money for you to keep on Mr and Mrs Bryant. Dora has always kept the old house in such good condition, and Fred has been working wonders here in the garden, too. In fact,' Liz had continued happily, 'it's nice to see the old house so well looked after.'

'Hmm. . .' Laura had agreed while casting a wry glance up at the roof, on which she had just spent many thousands of pounds.

There had been, of course, clearly nothing to be gained

by telling Liz all about all the hard, strenuous efforts required just to keep the bricks and mortar of the family home in good condition. Especially since by then Laura had been earning a great deal of money, and all the past difficulties had more or less been solved.

'It's great to know that the Manor House is always going to be here for you and your children, isn't it?'

'It's much more likely to be here for *your* children,' Laura had told her firmly. While she was deeply fond of Liz's twin girls—and had been thrilled to be chosen as their godmother—she was far too immersed in her role as a successful businesswoman even to consider the possibility of ever having any children of her own.

The sound of the distant chimes of Big Ben broke into her thoughts, and, on looking down at her watch, Laura gave a yelp of dismay. What on earth did she think she was doing, sitting out here on her balcony in the middle of the night? If there was one fixed rule in her life, it was to make sure that she had a regular eight hours' sleep every night. However boring the regime might sound, it was one that was absolutely essential. In fact, if she wanted to hold down her gruelling job in a profession that was notorious for being both fraught with tension and also for the high casualty rate of mental burn-out, she'd better try and get back to sleep—right now!

With a sigh, Laura left the balcony and walked back towards her bedroom. It was no good complaining. She'd known *exactly* what she was getting into when she had applied for a job with the commodity brokers, McKenzie Dunton. It had been her overwhelming need for money—*a great deal of money*—which had drawn her to the London Metal Exchange. After some time spent as a trainee, she had become an authorised dealer on the male-dominated floor of the Ring, specialising in the fast and furious world of copper futures. However, on her promotion last year as an executive consultant Laura had decided to concentrate more on her work in the office—analysing financial trends, and advising her private clients on their investments in the futures market.

There was no doubt that the rewards for someone in her profession were considerable. But so, alas, were the pitfalls—where one slip could cost millions of pounds, and result in her immediate dismissal. Even now that she had been made a director of the firm, Laura was well aware that it didn't mean that she had a job for life. She was no more secure than she'd ever been—one mistake, and she'd be out on her ear!

However, it had all seemed to be so very easy at first. Young and confident, she had traded millions of dollars' worth of metals without a thought. But now, with the City of London in a deep economic recession, the pressure on dealers had increased. Her job, which was already fraught with tension, had now also become one of almost overwhelming stress and strain.

Many of her colleagues had fallen by the wayside. And, if she didn't want to be a burnt-out case, too, she'd better try and get some sleep, Laura told herself roughly as she slipped into bed and turned off the light. Not only did she have that reporter to cope with in the morning, but if those rumours about the Russians planning to dump some of their copper stocks on the London market were true. . .? Well. . .it looked as if tomorrow might be a *very* hectic day indeed.

* * *

Hectic wasn't the word! There must surely be another, far stronger expression to describe this mayhem, Laura told herself, desperately trying to close her ears to the mind-blowing volume of noise around her. Juggling three phones at once, she attempted to concentrate on placing and receiving orders from clients scattered across the world.

'It's bedlam in this office! How on earth can you stand it?'

Laura turned to grin at the small dark-haired girl sitting beside her desk. Anita Jackson, the reporter from *Business Finance Magazine*, had turned out to be very pleasant and friendly—and not at all the terrifying type of eagle-eyed investigatory journalist of Laura's overheated imagination.

'I'd go mad if I worked here—absolutely around the bend!' the reporter shouted over the blaring noise of the loudspeakers, which were relaying market information to the other dealers in the large office. 'And I still can't work out exactly what it is you *do*. . .'

'Well, I'm basically a trader of futures,' Laura told her. 'That is, contracts to buy a commodity—mostly metals like copper and zinc, in my case—at a specified price on a specified date. The profit comes, as always, from buying low and selling high. And, I must say, it would have to be a very bad year if I didn't double my clients' money!' she added, before breaking off to answer more phone calls.

'I thought you'd just been made a director of this firm?' Anita Jackson asked, looking around the large crowded room in confusion. 'Shouldn't you have your own office?'

Laura laughed. 'This *is* my office,' she told the other girl, adding wryly, 'A directorship just means that you get a share of the profits—and your name on the letterhead, of course!'

The reporter shook her head, wishing she had some cotton-wool to put in her ears. 'Is it like this all day? Because, if so, I don't know how you can stand the pace!'

'It's a high-pressure job, and you burn out young,' Laura agreed, pointing to the numbers and letters scrolling constantly across a video screen above her desk showing the commodity prices in London, New York and Chicago. 'There you are—that's sterling, and that's gold. I'm also watching cocoa and Deutschmarks, platinum. . .wheat and pork bellies. I've got a position in soya, so I'm keeping an eye on that as well.'

Laura reached forward to answer one of the phones ringing on her desk. 'It's not too hard when you get into the rhythm of it,' she continued with a grin. And, while holding a conversation with her client, she was also listening to the voice of her broker, relaying prices from the floor of the Metal Exchange in Plantation House through the loudspeaker on the wall above her desk.

I wouldn't have this girl's job—not for all the tea in China! Anita decided firmly, gazing in amazement and considerable admiration as Laura juggled three phones at once, while placing and receiving orders from customers scattered across the world. When she'd been doing her research for this article she'd talked to various other people in the City regarding Laura Wyndham's expertise in her job, and they had all agreed on one thing—she was at the very top of her profession.

'"Luscious Laura" can be a real killer,' one of her male competitors had ruefully told Anita. 'If she sees a weakness in the market she's in there, and—pow! Splat! Laura has picked up her bargains and left the rest of us reeling, not knowing what's hit us!'

However, after spending some time amid the pandemonium of this noisy office, Anita had come to one definite conclusion: Laura might well earn an absolute fortune—reputedly a quarter of a million pounds a year—but, as far as Anita was concerned, she certainly deserved *every penny*!

Feeling battered in mind and body by the time Laura announced that she felt able to take a break—and how about an early lunch?—Anita could do no more than give her a dumb nod of agreement.

'I don't know about you,' the reporter was saying as they walked across the cool marble-floored lobby of the large office building and out into the hot, brilliant midday sunshine of Fenchurch Street, 'but I'd practically sell my soul for a really *icy cold* vodka and tonic. Or maybe a cool drink of. . .' Her voice trailed away as she saw that Laura had come to an abrupt halt beside her.

Following the other girl's fixed gaze, Anita noticed that a large black chauffeur-driven limousine was drawing up to the edge of the road. A second later a tall, broad-shouldered figure threw open the rear door— clearly too impatient to wait for the chauffeur to bring the vehicle to a halt. Jumping out on to the pavement, the man began striding swiftly towards them.

'What in the *hell* is going on? I've been trying to get hold of you for the past two hours!' the man exclaimed harshly as he stared down at Laura, who was gazing back at him as though she'd seen a ghost. 'Why haven't you been answering my phone calls?'

'I. . . I haven't had any calls from you,' Laura gasped, finally managing to find her voice at last. 'And. . .and I *certainly* wouldn't have answered them, even if I had!' she told him fiercely before spinning quickly around on her heels and beginning to walk rapidly away down the street.

And only *then*—as Anita Jackson was later to ruefully confess to her editor—did the reporter realise that she had a real, *genuine* scoop taking place in front of her very eyes.

Because the tall, dark and extremely handsome man— whom she only recognised as the mega-rich industrialist, Ross Wyndham when it was *far* too late to do anything about it!—seemed to move across the pavement with the speed of light. One minute he was just standing there— and the next instant he suddenly grabbed hold of Laura, quickly scooping her tall, slender body up into his arms before carrying the struggling figure of the girl towards his large limousine.

CHAPTER TWO

'WHAT's going on?' Laura cried, struggling to sit up on the wide leather rear seat of the large car, where she had been so unceremoniously tossed only a moment before.

'Relax. Calm down,' Ross drawled, joining her inside the vehicle and slamming the door behind him, before leaning forward to have a quiet word with the chauffeur.

'What do you think you're doing. . .? she gasped, still feeling shocked and disorientated by the sudden, totally unexpected appearance of the man she hadn't seen for so many years. 'Let me out of here—*at once!*'

When he took not the slightest notice of her demand Laura closed her eyes, forcing herself to breathe slowly and deeply as she desperately tried to pull herself together. Could she be in the midst of a hideous fantasy? Or maybe she was experiencing a sort of nightmare or hallucination—some kind of unfortunate delusion brought on by the overwhelming stress and strain of her job. . .?

But, unfortunately, she soon realised that *if* it was a nightmare it was a *living* nightmare. Because as she opened her eyes she could plainly see that there was nothing even remotely ghost-like about the tall, broad-shouldered figure of her husband, Ross Wyndham, now sitting on the seat beside her.

'But. . .but. . .why on earth are you kidnapping me like this?' she demanded breathlessly, feeling intimidated by his overwhelmingly strong physical presence. 'And where are we going?' she added, her eyes widening in apprehension as the limousine began moving swiftly through the narrow streets of the City.

'For goodness' sake, Laura—relax!' he ground out impatiently, quite obviously not accustomed to having his power and authority questioned in any way. 'I'm merely taking you——'

'"Merely". . .?' Laura gave a gasp of angry, incredulous laughter. 'I have no intention of being taken *anywhere* by you!' she told him fiercely, before turning to grab hold of the door-handle beside her.

Whether she would in fact have opened the door and tried to jump out of a moving vehicle proved to be an academic question. Because at that precise moment the chauffeur put his foot down hard on the brake as he made an abrupt, sharp turn down a narrow street, and Laura found herself being thrown backwards across the seat. . .into Ross's embrace.

'Let me out of here!' she spluttered helplessly as he tightened his arms about her slim figure, ignoring her struggles with contemptuous ease.

'My dear Laura,' he drawled smoothly, looking down at her flushed cheeks, the blue eyes glinting with indignation, and her full lips trembling with rage and fury. 'Believe me, you're not going anywhere!'

'I'm not s-staying here, in this. . .this c-car. . .' she stuttered, trembling as she felt the warmth of his hard, firm body through his thin silk shirt. Being pressed so tightly against his chest—with his handsome, tanned face only inches away from her own—was so evocative of the past that she began to feel quite faint and dizzy.

As she stared, mesmerised, up at his wide, sensual mouth, it seemed for one wild, completely mad moment that he was intending to kiss her. . .

And then, swearing briefly under his breath, Ross tightly gripped her arms. It was only when she found herself being abruptly swept off his lap, and on to the leather seat beside him, that she managed to start pulling herself together.

'I. . . I demand to be let out of here!' she cried in a shrill voice.

'I think you're beginning to repeat yourself,' Ross drawled smoothly. 'However, there's really no need for you to do so, since this is where we get out,' he added, opening his door and helping her stiff, angry figure out on to the pavement.

Laura looked around her with amazement. 'What on earth are we doing *here*?' she muttered, staring up at the familiar sight of an old converted warehouse overlooking the Thames.

'Surely this is where you have your apartment. . .?' Ross said, taking hold of her arm and leading her through the wide arched entrance of the building, towards a bank of lifts.

'Yes, but. . .' Laura blinked in confusion, raising a hand to push nervous, shaky fingers through her hair. Goodness knows what was happening to her, but she seemed to be trapped in some thick mental fog. She—who'd always prided herself on her clear, incisive brain—was now finding that her thought processes seemed to be completely jammed.

'How—er—how did you know that I lived here?' she

muttered as he led her inside the lift, reaching across to push the correct floor button.

Ross gave a short bark of grim laughter. 'Don't be so foolish, Laura. Since you are still technically my wife, I obviously know *everything* about you.'

The hard, flat, almost contemptuous note in his voice sent shivers of apprehension feathering down her spine.

He hadn't changed, she thought glumly, staring determinedly past his shoulder at the bright steel walls of the lift. Ross was obviously still the same hard, tough personality that he'd always been—never giving an inch in an argument, or showing any trace of the ordinary human weaknesses which affected everyone else.

In fact, she had never known *anyone* who exuded such arrogant, confident masculinity, such a strong conviction of his own superiority and worth. Even when they had first been married, Ross has always been quite determined that——

'Come on, give me your keys.'

'What. . .?'

She looked up, startled to find that they had already arrived at the top floor, and were now walking down the corridor towards her apartment. How on earth had they got up here? Oh, heavens! She *must* be losing her marbles, because she'd absolutely no recollection of what had been happening during the past few minutes. . .! Laura's cheeks flushed as she hunted in her handbag for her bunch of keys. You've got to pull yourself together! she lectured herself sternly as Ross took the keys from her nervous, trembling fingers.

'Look—er—this is all. . .well, it's all *quite* ridiculous,' she told him as he issued her into the apartment. 'I mean—what's the point of dragging me back here, to my own home?'

'I need to talk to you,' Ross told her curtly.

'Oh—come on!' she snapped nervously, turning around to face him as they entered the living-room. 'If you needed to see me—for any particular reason—there are thousands of places to meet in the City. We could have had a perfectly *civilised* meeting, and not this——'

'There was no time,' he said curtly, walking across the deep-pile carpet towards the wide floor-to-ceiling windows at the far side of the large room.

Laura's normally full, warm lips tightened with annoyance. How dared this man think that he could just move back into her life—after five long years—and then begin treating this place as if it were his own home? Well, it wasn't! It was *her* apartment, paid for with her own money, and she didn't need or want him in her life any more.

'OK, Ross,' she ground out. 'We've had the caveman impersonation, *and* your version of a minor kidnapping— so what's next on the agenda?'

Fighting hard to control her temper, Laura glared at her husband's tall figure. It didn't seem as if the awful man was listening to one word of what she was saying! Continuing to stand with his back to her, he stared silently down at the muddy green waters of the River Thames for some moments, before turning slowly around to face her.

'This is a pleasant room—very charming,' he murmured, clearly absorbed by his own inner thoughts as he glanced idly around at the cream carpet and the matching raw silk curtains edging the windows. The long oak refectory table gleamed with polish, and the comfortable sofas and deep armchairs were covered in pale, ice-cream colours of blue, pink and green, in cool contrast to the brilliant rays of the midday sun, now streaming in through the large windows.

'What did you expect—bare floorboards?' she snapped irritably, before taking a deep breath and striving to calm down. Goodness knows why he'd dragged her here—right in the middle of the day, for heaven's sake!—but there wasn't anything to be gained by losing her temper. 'Look, Ross, I still don't understand——'

'Why don't you sit down, Laura?' he said, moving slowly across the carpet towards her.

'Because I don't want to!' she informed him bluntly. 'I deeply resent being dragged away from my office for no good reason that I can see. *You* may have all the time in the world, but the rest of us have to earn a living. In fact,' she glanced impatiently down at her wrist-watch, 'the US markets are open now, and every minute that I'm away from my desk my clients are losing money.'

'Can't you think about anything else other than making money?' he growled.

'No, not at the moment,' she retorted. 'And, anyway, you're a fine one to talk!' she added defiantly, while backing nervously away from his advancing figure. 'When did the mega-rich Ross Wyndham ever think about *anything* other than the Wyndham International Banking Corporation. . .?'

His grey eyes narrowed dangerously. 'That's absolute nonsense, Laura!'

'Oh, no, it's not,' she responded bleakly. 'As far as

you were concerned, it was always business first and
foremost. Everyone else—particularly your wife!—came
a very bad second.'

'And what about your slavish devotion to your family?
When did you ever put *me* first in your life?' he demanded
angrily, before taking a deep breath and clearly making
a determined effort to pull himself together. 'However, I
did not come here to quarrel with you, Larua. If you'll
just sit down, and——'

'You still haven't told me what we're doing here,' she
protested.

'I told you to sit down!' he ground out through
clenched teeth, and when she didn't immediately obey
him he placed his hands on her shoulders, pushing her
firmly down on to a sofa.

'Well—really!' she fumed.

'I don't want any more nonsense,' he told her sternly.
'I have to talk to you—and I have to talk to you *now*.
It's very important, Laura.'

Just about to explode with fury, she suddenly caught
the oddly constrained, heavy note of tension in his voice.

In the pool of silence which fell between them Laura
raised her eyes and took her first good, clear look at the
man she had married, and whom she hadn't seen for so
many years.

Basically, of course, he hadn't really changed at all.
Ross Wyndham was all that she had tried so hard to
forget—and more: tall, lean, dark and almost painfully
attractive, his tanned skin darkened further by the thick
black hair, which was swept back like a lion's mane over
his well-shaped head before sweeping down to curl over
the top edge of his collar. He was, perhaps, slightly

thinner than she remembered, and, although he couldn't be more than thirty-five, there were now some faint silver threads among the dark hair at his temples. The steely granite-grey eyes beneath their deeply hooded lids were only part of his dark attraction. Set above an aquiline nose, they only hinted at the sensuality which was clearly evident in the curved line of his mouth and his hard, determined chin.

As she knew to her cost, his appearance accurately reflected his character: a hard, dangerous man who scarcely bothered to mask his raw, vibrantly physical aura of controlled savagery. A restrained virility that boded ill for anyone so incredibly foolish as to even think of challenging his authority. Her cousin Liz had always said that Ross reminded her of a ferocious, hungry lion gliding smoothly through the tall grass of life, looking for his supper! The fact that Liz had also said Ross was kind, overwhelmingly generous, and one of the sexiest men she'd ever met was not something that Laura wanted to think about at the moment.

She closed her eyes, taking an unsteady breath as she tried desperately not to recall the deeply tanned torso, the slim hips and the taut, firmly muscled thighs which lay beneath the dark Savile Row suit he was wearing with such ease and assurance.

Dropping her eyes and staring blindly at her nervously twisting hands, Laura tried to control the flush she could feel spreading over her pale cheeks, the betraying quiver of sexual awareness which had suddenly scorched through her body. How well she knew—and who better?—the devastating effect that this man's presence could have on the female population. It wasn't just the unmistakable aura of wealth and ruthless power which drew women to him like moths to the flame. Girls had obviously been standing in line for this man from the first day he'd put on long trousers—or even earlier, she thought grimly. Because it hadn't just been her preoccupation with her father's illness which had contributed to the breakdown of their brief marriage. His close, intimate relationship with his personal assistant, Marissa Kenton, had also been a major contributory factor.

'The fact is, Laura. . .' Ross's voice broke into her confused thoughts. However, when she raised her head to look at him once more he hesitated, giving a preoccupied shake of his head before beginning to pace up and down the carpet in front of her.

Although Ross was still obviously the same hard, unshakeable man who'd always been master of his own emotions, it did seem to Laura that he was now acting in an oddly constrained manner. She hadn't seen him for some years, of course, but she was sure that it wasn't like him to be so edgy. . .so extraordinarily tense and restless.

'What's the problem, Ross?' she asked. And, when he didn't immediately reply, she hesitated for a moment, taking a deep breath before adding, 'Do you—er—do you want to discuss a divorce?'

'A divorce. . .?' He paused in his restless pacing, raising a dark eyebrow as he stared at her intently. 'Why should I want a divorce?'

Laura gave a careless laugh, which even to her own ears sounded slightly shrill and off-key. 'Well, it has been a long time, and I expect you and Marissa. . .'

'Marissa?' He stared at her blankly for a moment.

'What the hell has Marissa got to do with any of this?' he demanded brusquely, frowning down at the flushed cheeks of the girl sitting on the sofa. 'I have not brought you back here to discuss a divorce, or any possible remarriage—to Marissa, or any one else!' he ground out harshly.

'Well, what *are* we doing here?'

He sighed heavily. Plunging his hands deeply into the pockets of his dark tailored suit, he frowned down at her from beneath his heavy brows, the lines of his face taut with strain and tension.

'Laura. . .' He sighed heavily again as he moved over to sit down beside her, leaning forward and burying his face in his hands for a moment.

And then—quite suddenly—she knew what he was trying to say.

There could only be one reason why Ross—always such a proud and unforgiving man—would have broken his own self-imposed exile and contacted her; only one reason why he would have brought her back to the quiet privacy of her own apartment.

'It's. . .it's Liz, isn't it?' she gasped. 'Something has happened to Liz. . .?'

He nodded his dark head. 'And Owen,' he said, his voice muffled by the hands still pressed to his face.

'Oh—*no*. . .!'

'Liz and my brother. . .' Ross began, a deep shudder shaking his tall frame. As he dropped his hands and turned towards her she was distressed to see the tortured expression deeply etched on his face. 'They were apparently going away for a long weekend vacation. It all happened in a few seconds. They never even had a chance,' he told her jerkily.

'But I don't understand. What's happened. . .?' she cried desperately.

'Apparently some mindless, stupid drunk careered straight into their car on the freeway. It's all right—they are still alive,' he said quickly, taking her limp hands within his own warm fingers, 'but they're both in Intensive Care in a hospital and no one seems sure if they'll be able to pull through. It's. . .well, it's all touch and go, I'm afraid,' he told her sadly.

'But. . .but the twins. . .?' Laura gasped, hardly able to comprehend that her cousin and his brother—a young, happily married couple—were now in danger of their lives. 'What about Emma and Sophie?'

'They're quite all right,' he murmured, placing a reassuring arm about her trembling shoulders. 'The twins are quite safe. The girls had already gone to stay with friends, who have a youngster the same age.'

'How. . .how did you hear about it?' she asked him, her mind in a complete daze.

'Their lawyer in New York contacted my mother.' Ross sighed and shook his head. 'She's totally devasted, of course.'

'Yes. . .yes, she must be,' Laura muttered, brushing a distracted hand through her blonde hair. She and her mother-in-law, Lady Nancy Wyndham, had always actively disliked one another. But now Laura could only feel a deep well of sympathy and compassion for the older woman.

'I'm sorry, Ross. I just can't somehow seem to. . .to take it all in,' she gasped, the magnitude of the disastrous tragedy suddenly beginning to penetrate her stunned mind.

Tears welled up in her eyes and began slipping slowly down her cheeks. As she raised a trembling hand to brush them away she heard him swearing softly under his breath. And then his arm tightened about her, pulling her quivering figure against his broad chest, while he raised a hand to gently stroke her smooth strands of fine golden hair.

'For God's sake, Laura,' he groaned. 'Please. . .please don't cry like this.'

'I. . . I just can't s-seem to help it,' she wept, unable to staunch the heavy flow of tears streaming down her pale cheeks.

For some time the only sound in the room was that of her choking sobs and his comforting murmur as he continued to tenderly stroke her hair. When the flow of tears slowly began to dry up she gratefully accepted the use of his handkerchief, drying her eyes and fiercely blowing her nose as she slowly raised her head from his chest.

'I'm sorry. I. . . I know this is just as hard for you— maybe harder, since Owen is your own brother. But. . .but Liz and I. . .' She gulped, unable to continue speaking as she fought to keep back the tears that were threatening to fall yet again.

Ross slowly withdrew his arm from about her shoulders, a muscle beating tightly in his jaw as he rose to his feet and walked across the room to where some bottles and cut-glass decanters stood on a tray. A moment later he had returned, and was holding out a balloon glass containing an inch of brandy towards her.

She shook her head. 'Oh, no—I couldn't possibly. I never. . . I mean, I only keep drink here for visitors.'

'Drink it!' he commanded roughly.

'No,' she protested, but when he continued to stand there, glowering threateningly down at her, she shrugged and took a small, cautious sip.

'That's a definite improvement—you look a lot better,' he told her bluntly as the strong liquor began flowing through her veins, and he saw a faint spark of colour beginning to tinge her pale cheeks. 'How do you feel now?'

'I. . . I'll be all right. It's just that it's all so. . .so awful,' Laura muttered helplessly. 'When will we know? I mean. . .when will we know if they're both going to be able to pull through?'

'I've no idea.' He shook his head sadly. 'Now, I'm going to have to be practical, I'm afraid. It's a terrible thing to have happened, but we have to be strong—if only for the sake of Emma and Sophie.'

She nodded. 'Yes, yes, of course, we must do what we can. What. . .what's going to happen to the children?'

'As you can imagine, my mother has completely collapsed. However, my personal assistant has been in touch with Carole and Ben Meadows. They are the couple who have been looking after the twins, and it was they who first contacted my mother earlier this morning. I've sent a message to say that we'll take care of the twins.'

'The poor little darlings.' Laura wiped her eyes and blew her nose loudly again. 'I. . . I'll certainly do my very best to look after them.'

'I thought that would be your immediate response.' He gave her a surprisingly warm glance of approval. 'So, while trying to contact you this morning, I made arrangements for us to fly to New York later on this afternoon. It wasn't easy, but I did manage to get practically the last two available tickets. Which means,' he added, glancing quickly down at the slim gold watch on his wrist, 'I want you to pack a suitcase as quickly as possible, because we have very little time in which to catch the plane.'

Laura looked at him in bewilderment. 'You're saying. . .you mean that you and I. . .we're both flying to America this afternoon?' She shook her head bemusedly, brushing a trembling hand across her brow.

'Yes, of course,' he told her impatiently. 'Emma and Sophie are only five years old. I can't possibly look after them on my own, and it's obvious that those two little girls are going to need a considerable amount of mothering.'

'But Ross—I don't know the first thing about children!' she exclaimed helplessly.

'That makes two of us!' he told her brusquely. 'In fact, what *I* know about children could be written on the back of a postage stamp. However, we're just going to have to do our best, right?'

Some time later, seated beside Ross as the chauffeur-driven limousine sped on its way to Heathrow Airport, Laura could feel her head beginning to throb and pound as the accumulated tensions of the day began to take their toll.

Rushing around the apartment like a madwoman, she'd hastily thrown some clothes into a case—and she could only pray that she hadn't forgotten anything vital. There had been so much else to do: such as leaving a brief note for Julie, and also contacting her office to explain the problem and that she'd be in touch with them as soon as possible. Luckily Tim Dunton had been very understanding, telling her not to worry and to take as long as she needed to sort matters out. He quite understood that there was no way she could have possibly refused to accompany Ross to New York. And, indeed, she was more than anxious to do what she could to help look after the twins.

However, she was finding it difficult to stifle the waves of panic which swept through her body at the thought of being in close contact with this man who had once meant so much to her. She was well aware that it would seem thoroughly feeble—if not downright pathetic—to refuse to accompany him to New York simply because they had been separated for almost five years. The initial alarm that had swept over her in the apartment had now settled down into a tight knot of almost sick apprehension, which lay like heavy lead deep in her stomach. Despite the call of duty, and the deep warm affection she had for her cousin's little girls, every instinct Laura possessed was overwhelmingly urging her to leave this vehicle; to put as great a distance between herself and Ross as she possibly could.

Laura's totally confused, unhappy thoughts were interrupted as she heard Ross clear his throat.

'It occurs to me. . .' he drawled, hesitating for a moment as he studied her intently from beneath his heavy eyelids, before turning his head to stare out of the window at the passing traffic. 'It occurs to me—especially since you mentioned a divorce—that you might feel slightly awkward about our trip to America.

However, our married life was so brief, and it took place so long ago, that it all now seems a matter of very little importance. Don't you agree?'

Laura glanced through her eyelashes at the thick dark hair curling over the edge of his collar, the relaxed set of his broad-shouldered figure as he continued to idly watch the passing scenery, while he talked so calmly and dismissively about a marriage which, it was quite clear, had never been of any major importance in his life.

'After all, so much has happened to us both in the last five years, hasn't it? We both now have far more important things to worry about than something which was merely a youthful—er—mistake, hmm?'

When put like that—what could she say? How could she possibly protest or put forward any arguments, when he was being so obviously sensible and reasonable?

Laura's normally sparkling blue eyes were cloudy and dull as their car approached the airport terminal. Desperately trying to pull herself together, she strove to console herself with the thought that, if Ross could hardly remember their brief marriage, it was obviously going to make matters easier for them both during this hurried trip to America. She turned to stare fixedly out of the window, furiously blinking away the moisture which was threatening to fill her eyes, and trying to ignore a large lump which seemed to have become stuck in her throat.

Moving like a sleep-walker through the efficient check-in at the first-class desk, through Passport Control and into the special lounge before boarding the aircraft, Laura felt totally numb. It was as if everything that had happened to her that day had some how taken place in another time dimension. And, despite the luxurious comfort of the aeroplane—in which she should have been able to relax her tired mind and body—she felt totally overwhelmed by the day's events.

Devastated as she was by the news of Liz and Owen's terrible accident—and the knowledge that their lives were hanging by a thread—she was also feeling dazed and stunned at her husband's dramatic reappearance in her life.

Maybe it was the hypnotic, rhythmic drone of the aircraft engines, or the sheer emotional exhaustion of the past few hours, but there seemed little she could do to suppress the memories she had so resolutely buried during the last five years. Memories of the past, which now filled her mind to the exclusion of all else.

CHAPTER THREE

IT WAS not difficult for Laura to remember the first time she had set eyes on Ross Wyndham, because it had also been the day of her cousin's wedding.

As the only bridesmaid, she had been following Liz up the aisle of the small country church, nervously clutching her bouquet of trailing greenery and praying that she wouldn't make the awful mistake of treading on the long train of Liz's wedding dress. It wasn't until they had come to a halt that she had felt able to raise her eyes from the floor and look at the two men standing by the alter rail.

While she recognised the figure of her cousin's fiancé, whom she'd met at their engagement party, the man standing beside him was a complete stranger.

Laura couldn't seem to tear her eyes away as she absorbed the man's hawk-like, tanned face and the sensual appeal of his tall, broad-shouldered body elegantly clad in a black long-tailed jacket and dark-striped trousers. As if he felt her gaze on him, the man slowly turned his head, a pair of steely grey eyes regarding her with a slow, almost insolent appraisal.

Nothing in her life so far had prepared Laura for the shock she experienced at the sheer animal magnetism projected by the stranger. Shivers tingled down the length of her spine, and she could feel herself trembling as her senses reeled beneath the assault of his forceful, raw masculinity.

She knew who he was, of course. While Owen's older brother, Ross Wyndham, had been abroad on business and unable to attend his brother's engagement party, he had faithfully promised to be Owen's best man at his wedding. But Liz had never mentioned that Ross was so staggeringly good-looking; nor had she made any reference to his devastating physical impact, although, to be fair, since both she and her cousin had only just finished taking their final college examinations, they'd hardly been able to spend any time together before the wedding.

Laura had learned that the newly married couple would be living in America, where Owen had obtained a position at Colombia University in New York. Not only was Liz looking forward to her new life in the United States, but also to living well away from her future mother-in-law. Apparently that imperious woman, Lady Nancy Wyndham, felt that her youngest son was marrying well beneath him, although her husband had been very kind and friendly.

'He's quite old now, of course, but Sir David Wyndham used to be a really big cheese in the business world. . .definitely a *grand fromage!*' Liz had giggled, before explaining that it was the eldest son, Ross, who now ran the family business—consisting of two merchant banks and many companies both here, in England, and abroad. When questioned about her fiancé's older brother, her cousin had merely giggled and replied that Laura would have to make up her own mind.

However, standing in the church behind her cousin, Laura could only think that Liz must be totally and blindly in love! Why had she chosen Owen and not Ross? How *could* she have failed to be knocked sideways by the man who, despite standing motionless and silent during the ceremony, appeared so effortlessly to dominate the proceedings?

In a dream-like trance, Laura drifted through the service and the reception, which was held in a large marquee in the garden of her parents' old home in Devon. Despite the hundreds of people present, she was almost painfully aware of Ross's tall dark figure as he glided smoothly, like a predatory animal, among the guests. He had barely addressed more than a few brief and studiously polite words to her—and yet every fibre of her being was vibrantly aware of his magnetic, almost menacing presence. Even when the happy couple had left for their honeymoon, and the floor of the marquee had been cleared for the dance due to follow the reception, she still felt as though she was wound up as tightly as a spring.

However, as the evening passed she began to relax. Quietly sipping champagne in a corner of the large marquee, Laura was just chiding herself for having overreacted in such a feeble, juvenile way towards a man who couldn't possibly be interested in her, when she looked up—and suddenly found Ross standing in front of her!

Looking impossibly handsome in his formal wedding clothes, he was surveying her with a fierce intensity that not only made her blush furiously, but caused her pulses to race almost out of control. For one heart-stopping moment she closed her eyes, feeling quite faint at the extraordinary nervous thrill of excitement and apprehension spiralling through her body.

And then his deep voice cut through the tense silence. 'You look like a wood nymph,' he drawled, his grey eyes beneath their heavy, sleepy lids gazing down at her flushed cheeks with sardonic amusement.

'Yes, I. . . I think that was meant to be the—er—general idea,' she muttered, staring down at her glass as she strove for composure. She'd always *known* that it wasn't her sort of outfit! Designed and made by one of her cousin's art school friends, the bridesmaid's dress was composed of many thin, floating layers of fine chiffon in soft shades of pale green and fawn. Fresh wild flowers had been woven through her long blonde hair, with more small blossoms strewn at random over the dress.

Aware that the dress had a fey, other-worldish air that was light-years away from her own rather down to earth personality, Laura gave a nervous shrug of her shoulders.

'I—er—I don't really think that this sort of thing is exactly my style,' she told him unhappily.

'You look ravishing—as if you've just stepped out of Botticelli's painting, *Primavera*,' he murmured. 'And I'm quite sure that you are exactly *my* style!' he added smoothly, removing the champagne glass from her trembling hand and setting it down on a nearby table. 'Shall we dance?' he asked her coolly.

She hesitated for a moment, before realising that to refuse would only make her appear ridiculous. She might secretly find this tall, elegant man extremely disturbing, but she wasn't prepared to let him guess that fact.

As he led her out on to the floor, and they began

moving together to the rhythm of the music, she desperately tried to relax her rigid, tense body. The silence between them seemed to last for eternity, and the longer it lasted, the harder it seemed to find something to say.

'How about the wedding? Or, of course, there is always the weather to fall back on. . .hmm?'

'What. . .?' Startled, Laura glanced quickly up at him, and met such a warm, infectious grin that she found herself smiling nervously back in return.

'I was merely suggesting two possible topics of conversation,' he drawled. 'However, such polite conventions are not necessary between us, since we are now—more or less—relatives by marriage. Although that particular relationship will become an even more intimate one very shortly.'

'It will. . .?' Laura frowned, glancing swiftly up at his tanned features, and she tried to work out the family ramifications. Since she and Liz were only cousins, her relationship to this dark stranger wasn't all that close, surely?

'Oh, yes.' He gave her a slow, sardonic smile. 'The French have a phrase for it: it's called a *coup de foudre*.'

Laura jerked her head back, staring at him in blank astonishment. 'But. . .but surely that means. . .?'

He nodded, giving her another slow, cynical smile. 'Yes,' he agreed. '"Love at first sight" is a very apt description of how I felt when I saw you in church today.'

'But. . .but that's not possible!' she gasped, her heart pounding with a strange excitement.

'I can assure you that it is,' he murmured gravely.

'That's ridiculous! I. . . I m-mean. . .you d-don't know anything about me,' she stammered.

Bitterly aware of a deep flush spreading over her cheeks, Laura closed her eyes for a moment as they continued to revolve around the dance-floor. She must—she really *must* try and pull herself together, very quickly. Even if he was joking—and yes, of course, he *had* to be—the proximity of his hard, lean figure and the elusive masculine aroma of his cologne were affecting her already dazed, confused senses in a thoroughly disastrous manner.

'You're quite wrong,' he told her firmly. 'Not only do I find you quite extraordinarily beautiful, but I also feel that I have known you all my life. And that, logically, leads me to the obvious conclusion—that I love you, and that we must be married as soon as possible. What more is there to say?'

Laura found herself reduced to silence, her heart pounding like a sledge-hammer. No one had ever talked to her like this before, and she wasn't at all sure how the game—if it really was a game—should be played.

She'd had plenty of admirers and boyfriends during her time at Cambridge, of course. But she'd been far too immersed in her studies, and had also been far too proud and fastidious, to experiment sexually with any of her contemporaries. This man was obviously considerably older than herself, and most of the women he knew would be likely to be as sophisticated and worldy-wise as himself. They would know how to conduct the sort of bright, clever and witty flirtation, full of sexual innuendoes and smart, amusing *double entendres*, that were well outside her own very limited experience.

However, he did not allow her to become too swamped with nervous, trembling uncertainty, as he began to talk calmly and reasonably about his brother's future life in America, describing some of the amusing mistakes he himself had made in assuming that the English and the Americans spoke the same language—when, in fact, so many words had different meanings. He was so funny and entertaining—and made her laugh and smile so much—that by the time he led her from the dance-floor, to fill their plates from the groaning buffet table, she felt far more relaxed and at ease.

'You were—er—you were just joking earlier, on the dance-floor—weren't you?' she murmured, not daring to raise her eyes as she toyed with some of the pink salmon mayonnaise on her plate.

Glancing over at the faint quiver in the hand holding her fork, and at the nervously fluttering long eyelashes, casting dark spiky shadows on her pale, trembling cheeks, he gave her a warm and reassuring smile.

'You're quite right, Laura. I really shouldn't have teased you as I did. Now,' he added, rising to his feet and taking the plate from her hand, 'it's a beautiful moonlit night—so why don't we take a walk in the garden, and you can tell me all about the history of your old family home?'

Strolling quietly together down the gravel paths of the old-fashioned Elizabethan knot garden, which was her mother's pride and joy, Laura found the evening taking on a completely different complexion. Ross made no attempt to touch her, other than to gently place his hand occasionally on her elbow as they walked around the house and garden. He was obviously interested in the

past history of the house, and, by the time they returned
to the dance-floor, all her irrational fears and instinctive
wariness of the tall dark man by her side had receded
into the very back of her mind.

In fact, from then on the rest of the evening seemed to
be bathed in a glorious, rosy light. She felt as if she were
floating on a soft, fleecy cloud, and quite sure that she
never wanted to return to earth. As Ross monopolised
her company, and claimed her for every dance, Laura
was dimly aware that not only were her friends amazed,
and frankly envious, but that she and Ross were the
focus of all eyes, and much gossip. But none of that
seemed to matter at all. The only important thing, as far
as she was concerned, was the gleaming silvery glow in
his hooded grey eyes, and the warmth of the hard body
pressed so closely to her own.

When the party eventually broke up Ross merely lifted
her hand to his lips, before leaving to join his parents at
their hotel, some miles away.

Sitting by her bedroom window later that night, Laura
lectured herself for having been so naïve as to have been
upset by the remarks he had originally made on the
dance-floor. She almost groaned aloud at her ignorance
in over-reacting in such a childish way to what,
obviously, he had only meant to be an amusing conver-
sational gambit. Her last depressing thought before she
fell asleep was that Ross must have been thoroughly
bored by her complete lack of sophistication, and it was
extremely unlikely that he would ever want to see her
again.

However, if Ross had been suffering from boredom,
he managed to hide the fact very well when, only a few

days later, he contacted her at the small London flat she was temporarily sharing with some friends from university, and invited her out to dinner.

Almost dancing on air, Laura had barely come down to earth when she found herself sitting beside him in a small riverside restaurant. There, as they looked out over the River Thames, he ordered a meal and demanded that she tell him her life story.

Laura could never remember what she had eaten that night. All she could recollect was that she'd been amazed to find that they'd been born on practically the same day in August: she on the sixth, and he on the eighth. She had also been surprised at how easy she had found it to talk to him, about all the private, intimate failures and successes of her life; fascinated to hear about his problems with the privately owned Wyndham International Banking Corporation, which he had recently taken over from his father. After gaining her economics degree at Cambridge she had been well able to appreciate some of the problems he faced, and ask pertinent, relevant questions about the business. In fact, so immersed in one another had they been that when they had looked up it was to find that all the other diners had left the restaurant.

Ross had taken her home, gently helping her out of the taxi and escorting her to the front door. Once again, he had merely kissed her hand before running back down the steps to the car, and roaring away into the night.

That had been the start of their relationship, which had so totally and dramatically changed her life. Through the following warm hazy days of summer,

Laura had realised that she was suddenly and magically in love, for the first time in her life. That Ross—so handsome, so much older and more experienced than she was—should be interested in her, had seemed to be almost a miracle beyond belief. However, as he had continued to see her, monopolising every free moment of her time, she had slowly come to accept that he was indeed 'interested'.

And yet. . .and yet. . .despite floating on cloud nine, Laura had found herself—most inexplicably—also beginning to feel extremely depressed. It was laughable, really, but when she looked back on her nervous apprehension regarding his overwhelming sexual magnetism she almost felt like weeping with frustration.

Although Ross had insisted on seeing her every day, during that time he had never done anything more than kiss her hand. And the intensity of her longing for him to press his mouth to her lips, or to be roughly crushed within his embrace, was becoming almost more than she could bear. She simply didn't know how to cope with the strange, inexplicable feelings of desire which were increasingly racking her mind and body. Was this what writers and poets meant by love? This wild, hectic, almost shocking excitement. . . a bitter-sweet, desperate longing that seemed to turn her limbs to water whenever she thought about Ross?

So what was wrong with her? she asked herself for the hundredth time as she sat sipping a glass of wine in his apartment in the Barbican some weeks after they'd first met. Soon after she had arrived here, this evening, he'd been forced to go to his study to take a transatlantic telephone call. And, as the long minutes ticked by while he was still busy on the phone, she defiantly poured herself another glass of wine. Ross seemed to want her company—he demanded it, in fact. And yet, when they were together, he insisted on treating her with a cool, bland charm which left her feeling baffled and frustrated.

'I'm sorry to keep you waiting.' Ross's voice broke through her unhappy thoughts, his dark eyebrows raised as he saw the half-empty wine bottle on the low table in front of her. 'Drinking too much wine on an empty stomach really isn't a very good idea,' he murmured.

'I don't care!' she told him rebelliously, scowling unhappily down at the small amount of red wine still in her glass. 'I'm just so miserable and fed up, and. . .' She sighed heavily.

'What's wrong, Laura?' he asked, coming to sit down beside her on the black leather sofa. And when she didn't reply he placed a hand beneath her chin and turned her face towards him. 'Tell me!'

The harsh command in his voice startled her. Raising her unwilling eyes to his, she saw that he was looking down at her intently, his grey eyes shadowed, a slight twist to his lips, as if he was trying to read her face.

She wasn't sure how long they stared into one another's eyes. The fumes from the amount of wine she had consumed seemed to be clouding her brain. He raised his hand to stroke the soft skin of her cheek, his eyes never leaving hers as she stared blindly back at him, her pulses seeming to almost race out of control. He was regarding her questioningly, searching her face as if it could tell him something. And when she did not move or draw back, he gave a heavy sigh.

'I think. . .yes, I really think that I have been far too

cautious,' he murmured quietly, before slowly and deliberately taking her into his arms.

The lips that touched hers were firm and warm. And,
as their pressure increased, Laura felt a brilliant light
seeming to explode in both her mind and body.
Instantly, as if he had somehow thrown an electrical
switch, she felt a surge of responsive excitement—so
strong and so unexpected that she trembled involuntarily
in his embrace.

At once his kiss seemed to deepen. His arms tightening
around her, he clasped her tenderly to his hard body
with an intoxicating mixture of desperate longing and
tender protectiveness. And then, almost at once, his iron
control seemed to snap, and he was kissing her with a
frenzied, pent-up, impatient longing that was totally
beyond anything she'd ever experienced before. Laura's
mouth parted beneath the soft pressure of his tongue as
he groaned against her lips. Fire raced through her
blood, her slim arms winding themselves instinctively
about his neck, the throbbing of his heartbeat seeming
to echo that of her own. Her lips felt swollen from his
kiss, her body shuddering as she felt his hand, pressed
tensely against her spine, hesitate for a moment and
then, as if he could not stop himself, slide around
caressingly over her slender body and up to the full swell
of her breast.

His fingers moved gently and delicately up over her
nipple, swollen and thrusting against the thin silk of her
dress, and all at once she felt a startling, sharp thrill of
pleasure as the enlarged aureole hardened beneath his
hand. As she gave a helpless moan his kiss grew gentler,
and he placed his arm once more about her soft body to

hold her cradled against him. His lips moved on hers lightly, and then he drew back.

Her eyelids slowly fluttering open, Laura trembled as she stared up at his grave face, his expression now troubled and curiously stern. Hesitating for a moment, he leaned forward and buried his face in her cloud of golden hair.

'Something happened when I first saw you.' His voice was muffled as his arms tightened involuntarily about her. 'I felt as if I knew you, and you knew me—almost from the beginning of time. It was as if, between you and I, the ordinary processes of—what shall I call it. . .courtship?—were totally superfluous.'

Slowly he loosened his arms, leaning her back against the back of the leather sofa, his granite-grey eyes searching her face.

'But I realised that I had spoken too soon,' he continued. 'That, if I wasn't very careful, I would frighten you away. And, although I was instantaneously and utterly in love with you—and quite determined that we should marry as soon as possible—I have been trying my damnedest to keep some kind of control over my emotions.'

While he had been talking the urgency of his hands on her body had increased, his thumbs moving up to softly circle the tips of her breasts, his eyes never leaving her face, as if he was carefully gauging her reaction. Laura gasped, the blood seeming to rush through her veins with a new, heady warmth. She could feel her nipples hardening beneath the touch of his fingers, and her body trembled almost uncontrollably. His deliberately quiet voice, and the apparent detachment with which his hands were moving over her body, frightened her and yet at the same time heightened the eroticism of the moment. She stared back at him, a total and willing victim of his dark physical presence, aware of nothing but the low sexual note in his voice and the excitement engendered by the slow stroke of his hands.

'I wanted you. I had to have you—and yet I hesitated. But, unfortunately, I don't seem to have any self-control left,' he told her, a small, bitter smile playing about his lips. 'I'm nine years older than you, Laura. You're so young and so very innocent—so completely untouched. I've always known that it would be wrong, almost criminal of me to take advantage of such innocence. . .'

'But. . .but I love you!' she cried, suddenly coming out of the trance in which she had been imprisoned, and desperately anxious that she should in some way communicate her feelings for him. 'I've been nearly going mad! I thought there was something wrong with me— that you weren't interested.'

'*Not interested?*' His harsh bark of laughter seemed to echo around the room. 'My God! If you only knew!'

'But I do!' she exclaimed, almost throwing herself back into his arms, and frenziedly clasping her hands about his neck. 'Oh, Ross—I love you with all my heart!'

'*Laura*!' he breathed thickly, his lips moving down over her soft cheek to the pulse at the base of her throat. 'I love you. . .and I want you to marry me—very soon. . .'

'As soon as possible,' she sighed ecstatically, hardly able to breathe as she felt his strong hands slowly undoing the zip of her dress, shuddering with excitement at the touch of his fingers against her bare skin. Her desperate need of him was so immediate, so pressing and urgent—and so incredibly familiar, as if it was the most natural thing in the world.

'Ross. . .' she gasped as he lowered her dress, his fingers tracing the pale blue veins in her full breasts, quivering as she glanced down to see his tanned hands moving slowly over her pale, alabaster skin. And when he bent his head, first to one breast and then the other, his lips closing over her swollen nipples, she felt as though she was almost going to die of excitement.

'Ross. . .!' she cried desperately. 'If you don't make love to me—here and now—I think I'll just *die*!'

Her desperate words provoked a great shout of laughter from him, and, holding her firmly in his arms he rose and carried her towards his bedroom. Barely pausing in his stride to kick open the door, he placed her tenderly down on his large bed.

'I love you, my darling Laura,' he murmured, before joining her on the bed and drawing her gently back into his arms. 'I'd never do anything to hurt you,' he added softly, slowly lowering his head until his mouth touched hers. In a daze of ever-increasing passion, she barely noticed as he gently removed her clothes, suddenly glad to be free of them and astonished to find herself revelling in his softly whispered murmurs of delight, the fierce gleam in his grey eyes, before first his fingers and then his lips began tracing patterns of fire on her quivering flesh.

Why had no one told her it would be like this? Laura wondered in a daze as he swiftly divested himself of his own clothing, and then, in the grip of a feverish, shuddering excitement, she responded as his lovemaking became more pressing and urgent. A deep, throbbing ache in the pit of her stomach seemed to obliterate everything except the overwhelmingly compulsive, driving need for his total possession. But it wasn't until she was almost driven out of her mind, delirious and sobbing with pleasure as she moaned his name, writhing helplessly beneath his intimate touch, that he moved to cover her body with his own. Barely noticing the brief, sharp moment of pain as her flesh yielded to his, she was caught up in a maelstrom of whirling sensations, the hard, pulsating rhythm drawing her down into an emotional whirlpool, before her body was suddenly racked by shuddering convulsions of a pleasure so incredibly intense that it was almost too much to bear.

Some time later, as she lay quietly enfolded in his arms, she felt him gently brushing the damp hair from her forehead.

'Are you all right, darling?' he whispered softly. 'I didn't mean to hurt you.'

'No. . .no, you didn't.' She levered herself up on an elbow, gazing down at his handsome, tanned face. 'I had no idea! I mean. . .' She laughed and threw herself back on the pillows. 'Oh, Ross—it was *so* terrific! Why did nobody tell me it was like this?'

He laughed. 'Because, my darling, it very rarely is,' he told her huskily, trailing his fingers over her soft, yielding flesh. 'What you and I have just had. . .what we have just experienced. . .well, I can tell you that it is something very special indeed. Maybe, if we are very lucky,' he continued as he drew her hungrily back into his arms, 'maybe for you and me it will always be like this.'

And it was. Their marriage, which had followed soon afterwards, was a very quiet, low-key affair. Although Laura would have liked a grand white wedding with all the trimmings, her mother had suddenly been taken ill, and clearly couldn't manage all the organisation necessary for such an affair. And so, after they'd just slipped off to the local registry office in the city, they had left for a brief honeymoon in Paris.

Those few brief months after their marriage had been a truly wonderful period of emotional bliss and happiness. Ross had been adamant that no wife of his was going to work. And so, although Laura would have liked to put her university degree to some good use, she had been so madly in love with her husband that she had willingly bowed to his wishes.

Despite being desperately busy with his business affairs, Ross had been infinitely patient and gentle, taking all the time in the world to skilfully lead her onwards to further erotic, rapturous delights of sexual fulfilment. And beneath his skilful touch she had learned to disregard all her virginal inhibitions, to respond with wanton delight to their mutual passion.

Now, as the throbbing drone of the aircraft's engines broke through her dark memories, and she wearily attempted to make herself more comfortable in her seat, Laura almost groaned aloud when she looked back at the total innocence and naïveté of her much younger self. How incredibly silly and pathetic she'd been. How childish of her to think that a good sexual relationship was all that was required for a successful marriage. But, all those years ago, she simply hadn't been experienced enough to realise that, despite those wonderful and ecstatic nights of passion, her marriage to Ross had been founded on a disastrously thin layer of quicksand; a relationship which would crack and disintegrate under the first onslaught of any stress and tension.

And there certainly had been a great deal of stress and tension—almost from the first few weeks following their wedding: Lady Nancy Wyndham's total opposition to their marriage; her own mother's sudden untimely death, followed by her father's long-drawn-out and eventually terminal illness; the total immersion of Ross in his business affairs, and—the final catalyst—the affair between Ross and his personal assistant, Marissa Kenton. No wonder their marriage had buckled beneath the strain! Even *one* of those items would have put a heavy stress on a new, fragile relationship. Maybe, if she had been a little older or more sophisticated, she might have been able to cope with what had seemed at the time to be a never-ending series of disasters.

Turning her head sideways, Laura gazed at the man reclining in his seat beside her. Even when dozing, there was no relaxation in her husband's ruthlessly hard, stern features—no apparent softening of his intimidating and menacing personality. He did, in fact, look every bit as formidable in his sleep as he did when awake.

She'd been so certain that, as the years went by, she would at last have broken free of his spell. So why did she now feel this frightening apprehension—a deep, numbing fear of what lay ahead?

CHAPTER FOUR

HOT, sticky and feeling utterly exhausted, Laura stood leaning weakly against the open door, while Ross carried their luggage into the apartment.

It wasn't just the flight to New York, the tedium of the long-drawn-out customs and transport formalities, and the helicopter trip between JFK airport and Manhattan that had been so tiring. It was her deep sorrow and unhappiness at the tragic accident that had brought them to the United States, together with all the fraught, highly charged tension of having to be in Ross's company for any length of time, which had taken its toll of her already precariously weak reserves of strength.

Gaining entrance to the large building had, also, taken a considerable amount of time and effort. Luckily Ross had at last managed to convince the superintendent of the large apartment block that they had a genuine, urgent need to enter the building—and to supply them with a spare key to the front door.

Grumbling under his breath at the lateness of the hour, and the fact that he was missing an important baseball game on TV, the super—who appeared to be of Polish extraction—nevertheless insisted on taking them up in an antiquated, dangerously shaky lift.

'I sure am sorry to hear about Mr and Miz Wyndham,' the fat man had wheezed, sorting through a large bunch of keys outside the battered-looking front door of the apartment. 'There you go,' he had added, opening the door and then handing the key to Ross. 'Have a good holiday.'

'What on earth does he mean by "holiday". . .?' Laura had muttered as Ross had picked up their suitcases.

'I imagine he was referring to the Independence Day celebrations,' her husband had told her as he'd led the way into the apartment.

Now, as she wearily trailed behind him into the main living-room, Laura's nose wrinkled at the musty, stale atmosphere of the room.

'It's so *hot*!' she exclaimed breathlessly. 'Maybe we could open a window, or——'

'No—you'd find it even hotter if we did,' he told her firmly, placing their suitcases down and switching on two small lamps on the tables set either side of a large, shabby couch which had clearly seen better days.

Immediately the room took on a more homely, comfortable appearance. The rather frayed drapes, either side of the tall windows, had a silky sheen in the soft lamplight, the scratched furniture and the thread-bare state of the rugs no longer as visible as they had been under the brilliant glare of the harsh overhead light.

Deeply ashamed of her first instinctive reaction to the obviously dilapidated and slightly scruffy room, Laura realised that her cousin Liz had created a warm, relaxing atmosphere—light-years away from her own, rather sterile, apartment back in London. Shaken to have found herself so suddenly envious of Liz's happy home life, and startled to realise that no amount of money could create these comfortable surroundings, Laura was jerked back to reality by the sound of Ross's voice.

'Why don't you take off your jacket? You'll be a lot cooler without it.'

He put out his hand towards her. As his fingers casually brushed her neck Laura froze, her nails biting into the palms of her hands at the sudden, shuddering quiver that zigzagged like lightning through her tired body.

'Are you all right?' he asked with a frown as she spun jerkily around to face him.

'Yes. . .yes, I'm fine. Just a bit tired, that's all,' she mumbled as she shrugged off her jacket.

He regarded her in silence for a brief moment. 'I should think that, like myself, you're feeling exhausted. The sooner I can get the air-conditioning on, the better,' he said, taking off his own jacket before going over to inspect the rather antiquated unit, set in the lower frame of one of the windows.

Compelled by an urgent desire to wash her travel-stained hands, Laura decided to investigate the layout of the rest of the apartment.

Liz had been quite right. It was indeed very small, even if not quite the 'shoe-box' proportions to which her cousin had jokingly referred. Other than the main living-room—with its round table and chairs in one corner, clearly doubling as a dining-room—it also contained two bedrooms, separated by a large family bathroom.

Smiling as she surveyed the posters on the walls of the twins' bedroom—obviously Peter Rabbit was still popular here in New York!—she moved on to the much larger main bedroom. Gazing longingly at its wide, comfortable bed, she heard Ross calling her name.

'I don't seem to be getting anywhere with this damn machine,' he said with exasperation. 'Why don't you fix us both a drink while I'm trying to find the answer to the problem?' he added, stripping off his tie and undoing the top buttons of his shirt.

Eventually tracking down some bottles of alcohol in the kitchen, she popped her head back around the door to ask Ross what he wanted.

'Anything—just as long as it contains a strong dose of alcohol!' he told her crisply, continuing to stand with his back to her, frowning down at the irritatingly silent machine.

Glancing at his figure, Laura felt the old longing for him twist like a knife in her stomach. The sight of his long, lean body, the cotton shirt stretched tightly over the blades of his broad shoulders, tapering down to a slim waist, brought back with sharp intensity a familiar ache in her body. She was aware that, even standing there, rolling up the sleeves above his tanned, muscular arms as he pondered the problem before him, Ross still possessed that sinister stillness, the iron self-control that had always set him apart from any one else she had ever known. And, even from across the room, she was almost tangibly aware of his aura of strong sexual magnetism.

Oh, no! She wasn't going to let him affect her like this—*never again*! she told herself desperately, taking a deep breath as she tried to ignore her racing pulse. You're just tired and exhausted, she told herself firmly, forcing herself to walk calmly across the room to hand him a glass.

'I could only find a bottle of bourbon and some after-dinner liqueurs,' she told him, being careful to avoid contact with his hand. 'Maybe. . .maybe there's a central switch somewhere?' she added.

'Now that's an idea,' he agreed slowly, giving her a cold smile that lifted his lips, but did not quite reach his eyes. 'Maybe you really *do* have that fast, incisive mind I've been hearing so much about lately?'

Ignoring the heavy irony of his voice, and deciding that she was just too weary to rise to the bait, Laura merely shrugged her shoulders.

'Shouldn't we telephone those people looking after the twins?' she asked. 'And I would like to get in touch with the hospital—to see how Liz and Owen are getting on.'

He nodded. 'I was just trying to get this infernal machine to start—to make us slightly more comfortable in here. However, you're quite right, of course,' he added, before lifting the glass to his mouth.

Hastily averting her eyes from the strong arched column of his tanned throat as he emptied his glass, she retraced her steps to the kitchen. She didn't normally drink any alcohol, but, if there was ever a time that she stood in need of hard liquor, this was definitely it! Tipping down her throat a large measure of neat bourbon, she gasped, leaning weakly against the wall and shuddering as the fiery liquid scorched its way down into her stomach. And then, feeling slightly light-headed from the Dutch courage, Laura returned to the living-room.

'I've just had a quick word with Carole Meadows,' Ross told her as he put down the phone. 'Apparently Emma and Sophie are fine—bearing up very well—

although Mrs Meadows says that she hasn't done any more than to tell the children that their parents have had a slight accident. She feels that there's no point in alarming the twins unduly at this stage.'

Laura nodded. 'That sounds sensible,' she agreed.

'I told her that we'd ring again first thing tomorrow morning. We'll then have heard from the hospital and can decide what to do about the situation. All right?'

'What about the hospital?' Laura asked, brushing a weary hand through her hair.

'I haven't managed to get through yet,' he said, studying her face intently from beneath his heavy eyelids. 'You look exhausted—absolutely all in. Why don't you go and lie down?'

Laura shook her head stubbornly. 'No, I couldn't possible rest, not until I've got an up-to-date report on Liz and Owen. And, besides. . .' She hesitated, wondering exactly how to broach the subject of their sleeping arrangements.

'There's no need for you to worry. I'll let you know as soon as I hear anything,' he told her with a surprisingly warm, reassuring smile. 'We're both obviously suffering from jet-lag, and we'll feel a lot better after a decent night's sleep.'

'I'm sure you're right—but we do have a problem,' she told him nervously. 'The thing is. . .well, this apartment only has two bedrooms. . .'

'That hardly sounds like a problem when there are only two of us,' he drawled sardonically.

'It is a problem—when the second bedroom only contains two small bunk beds,' she retorted, bitterly aware of the colour rising over her cheeks beneath the steady gaze of those cynical grey eyes.

Ross gave a bark of harsh, mocking laughter. 'I can assure you, my dear Laura, that I have neither the inclination nor the energy to lay my hands on your fair body,' he drawled sardonically. 'In fact, making love to you is just about the very *last* thing on my mind at the moment.'

Her face became hot with embarrassment beneath the cynical gleam in his heavy-lidded eyes. Trying desperately to preserve what shreds of dignity she still possessed, Laura lifted her chin. 'Relax—I wouldn't touch *you* with a barge-pole' she told him scornfully. 'But it *is* awkward. I was merely trying to sort matters out, and——'

'Oh, for goodness' sake, Laura!' he retorted angrily. 'I'm just too damn tired to put up with any nonsense— especially something so totally unimportant—at a time like this.'

Laura flinched. He was right, she realised, her cheeks flushing with mortification at having behaved in such a childish manner. Who slept where was a totally irrelevant question—particularly when compared to Liz and Owen's tragic accident and the plight of their two young children.

'I'm sorry,' she muttered. 'I just didn't think. I. . .'

Ross sighed, brushing his hands roughly through his thick dark hair. 'It's been a long, exhausting day, and we're both completely bushwhacked,' he said flatly. 'I can see that it's going to take me some time to get an answer from the hospital, and I have yet to sort out this business of the air-conditioning. So, since there's nothing

you can usefully do at the moment, you'd better go and
lie down.'

'I still feel that I ought to——'

'For God's sake—go to bed, Laura!' he growled,
taking a threatening step forward.

'OK, OK!' she mumbled breathlessly before quickly
picking up her suitcase and making her way into the
large bedroom.

There was clearly no point in arguing with the man
any longer, she consoled herself, wearily removing her
short-sleeved ivory silk blouse and the skirt of the pin-
striped navy suit in which she'd gone to work that
morning. She slipped on a thin gauze nightgown, and,
despite the clammy, stifling heat of the night, she
couldn't help shivering with exhaustion as she drew back
the bed cover, and crawled gratefully between the thin
cotton sheets.

Laura's last conscious thought was that she would
have no trouble in sleeping for a week. But the trauma
of the past twenty-four hours had clearly taken its toll.
For, at some point during the night, she awoke from a
restless sleep, to find her face and pillow damp with
tears. As she lay blinking blindly into the unfamiliar
darkness, her ears filled with a strange background hum,
her tired and sleepy brain slowly realised that the sound
which had awoken her had been her own desperate
sobbing.

She was dimly aware of someone—or something?—
brushing the wet tears from her face, of hard yet
comforting arms enfolding her trembling body as a low
deep voice murmured soothing words of comfort. A far
distant bell in her exhausted mind seemed to be ringing

some kind of warning. But the sheer warmth and solace of the strong arms about her were so reassuring that a few moments later she drifted off into a much calmer and deeper sleep.

'Wakey-wakey!'

Slowly struggling up from the depths of deep unconsciousness, Laura flicked open her eyelids, only to shut them firmly again as she winced at the brilliant sunshine flooding in through the windows of the bedroom. Alerted by a slight sound, she again opened her eyes, turning her head slowly to see a cup and saucer being placed on a nearby small table. Raising her gaze, she saw Ross's tall figure standing beside the bed.

'I see you are awake—at last!' He smiled down at her. 'I've made you a cup of coffee—and I should drink it while it's still hot, if I were you.'

Laura gave a low moan as she struggled to sit up, one half of her still almost unconscious mind noticing that Ross must have recently had a shower, since his black hair was still damp and he was wearing nothing but a short white towel about his waist. The bright shafts of sunlight seemed to cast a golden glow over his tall, lithe figure, illuminating the smooth, tanned skin rippling over the muscles of his arms and broad shoulders, the light mat of dark hair covering his deep chest.

'Er—wha-what time is it?' she mumbled, her mind too sleepy and uncoordinated to cope with the sharp, quivering response that gripped her stomach as she blinked nervously up at her husband.

'It's only nine o'clock—but we have a lot to do this morning,' he said briskly. 'I was in touch with the hospital late last night, and again this morning. I know that you'll be glad to hear there's a slight improvement in the condition of Liz and Owen. Apparently they're holding their own—and, in fact, doing slightly better than anyone expected.'

'Oh—that's marvellous!' she gasped with relief.

'I suggest that we pay a visit to the hospital this morning—although I'm not sure whether we'll be allowed to see Liz and Owen. They may be still too ill to see visitors,' he warned gently, bending down to hand her the cup and saucer.

'Yes, I do realise that,' she muttered, staring down at the brown liquid in the cup. 'But we must try and see them—if only to let them know that we're here, in the States, and that they have no need to worry about Emma and Sophie.'

He nodded. 'I think it might be a good idea if you were to contact Mrs Meadows this morning, and make arrangements for us to see the twins.'

'Yes—yes, of course,' she murmured, taking a quick, nervous sip of coffee as he sat down on the bed beside her.

'However, the good news is that I managed to find the switch for the air-conditioning. It appears to be working in both the bedrooms and the kitchen but not, alas, the main sitting-room.' He shrugged his bare shoulders. 'I might try and get the superintendent of this building to check it over for us later on this morning.'

'That's a good idea. It certainly seems a bit—er—cooler in here,' she told him breathlessly, her hands trembling at his proximity.

'Poor Laura—you never were any good at getting up

in the morning, were you?' he mocked softly, taking the clattering cup and saucer from her shaking hands, before leaning forward to brush a stray tendril of hair from her brow.

'No. . .' she muttered huskily. 'No, I wasn't. But, I'm much better now, I. . .' She found she couldn't continue, nor was she able to tear her gaze away from the dark, silky hair on his chest, only inches away from her eyes. The blood seemed to be pounding in her sleepy head, her heart racing almost out of control as she felt the smooth passage of his finger slipping down her throat, slowly brushing the thin strap of her gown from her shoulder. Closing her eyes as her senses seemed to be spinning giddily out of control, she was unaware of his eyes devouring the sheen of her pale skin, gleaming like alabaster in the warm morning light, and the sight of her full breasts rising erotically above the now lowered neckline of her gown.

'How could I have forgotten the wonderfully smooth, velvety texture of your skin?' he whispered huskily, raising his other hand to gently caress her soft shoulders.

Her body seemed determined to ignore the danger signals now at last flashing through her brain. There was no resistance from her as his hands moved caressingly over her flesh, her senses somehow drugged and seduced into quivering acquiescence as he leaned forward, trailing his lips down over her throat and lower neck, searching for and finding the firm, warm swell of her breast.

'*Laura*. . .!' A deep groan broke from the depths of his throat as he lifted her trembling figure towards him, crushing her body ruthlessly to his hard bare chest, his mouth closing over her trembling lips in a kiss of fierce, urgent possession.

Just for a moment she ignored the by now loud warning sirens wailing at the back of her mind. Abandoning herself to the overpowering intoxication of his embrace, she parted her lips beneath his as he ravished the inner sweetness of her mouth. For one brief moment it felt as though she was almost drowning in ecstasy, and then she felt Ross removing his lips, cursing violently under his breath as he withdrew his arms from about her body. Her eyelashes fluttering as the thick mists of her desire began to dissolve, she, too, caught the strident sound of the telephone, ringing loudly in the other room. A second later he had levered himself up off the bed, striding away to answer the call.

Grabbing the sheet, and hauling it tightly up under her chin, Laura lay back, gasping, against the pillows, her brain filled with a seething mass of conflicting emotions.

You total, *utter* fool! she told herself grimly, desperately trying to control her trembling figure. What on earth could have possessed her? Surely she knew that it was *fatal* to let Ross anywhere near her? Because he wasn't just the same hard, tough personality that he always had been: he was now *far* more dangerous—certainly if her present fragile emotions were anything to go by. She hadn't seen him for almost five years and yet—*less than twenty-four hours later*—she'd been not only happily returning his kisses, but also moaning with pleasure at the feel of his hands on her body.

You must be absolutely and totally out of your tiny mind! she told herself fiercely, ashamed that, despite the apparent sophistication of her twenty-five years, she should have succumbed so quickly to his dark, fatal attraction.

Laura was still roughly chastising herself, and attempting to ignore the hard knot of unsatisfied desire still gripping her body, when Ross came back into the room.

'Was that. . .was that the hospital?' she asked, a numbing dread about the fate of her cousin suddenly driving all else from her mind.

'No.' He shook his head. 'That was merely a call from London. Just my personal assistant bringing me up to date on some business matters,' he added dismissively as he walked over to the other side of the bed, picking up his slim gold watch from a small table.

Turning her head towards him, Laura glanced down at the rumped sheets on the mattress beside her. 'Did. . .did you sleep here beside me last night?' she demanded huskily, although she had a sinking feeling that she already knew the answer.

He shrugged his shoulders. 'Yes, of course I did.'

'But I made it quite clear that I wasn't prepared to share a bedroom with you!' she retorted angrily.

'So you did,' he drawled smoothly, slipping the gold watch on to his bronzed wrist. 'But, even if I had felt inclined to do so, there was no way I could have got a decent night's rest on those small, short bunks next door.'

'There's a perfectly good sofa in the living-room,' she protested. 'Any man with an *ounce* of sensibility and tact would never have——'

His deep rumble of sardonic laughter cut across her

words. 'Oh, come on, Laura! Even if I were a man of deep sensibility and tact—and it sounds pretty wimpish to me!—I still needed a good night's sleep. And besides,' he added in a mocking drawl, 'you seemed remarkably grateful and content in my arms last night!'

'Last night?' she echoed faintly, before suddenly recalling a dim memory of being held within a pair of comforting arms.

'Ah, I see the light is beginning to dawn,' he murmured, raising a dark, cynical eyebrow, his lips twisting with amusement as he saw her eyes widening in dismay.

'You didn't. . .?' she gasped, her cheeks growing pale as his words struck home. 'I mean, we didn't really. . .?'

'Make love?' He grinned, clearly enjoying her acute discomfiture. 'No, I'm afraid we didn't. Although, of course, it's only a matter of time until we do.'

Laura could scarcely believe her ears. 'You must be joking!' she lashed back huskily. 'Even if you were the last man on earth—I wouldn't make love to you,' she added bitterly.

'But, my dear Laura, that's *exactly* what you were doing—only five minutes ago!'

As his sardonic laugh echoed around the bedroom Laura suddenly realised how some people were driven to murder their tormentors. Bitterly aware of a deep tide of crimson flooding over her face and body, she could only glare back at him with deep loathing. After all, what could she possibly say? There was no disputing the hard truth behind his words—someting for which she had already severely upbraided herself.

While she was desperately trying to think of something—anything!—in explanation of her own folly the opportunity passed as he turned to leave the room.

'I'm going to get dressed in the twins' room, and I suggest you do the same in here, as quickly as possible. There are a great many things we have to do today,' he added over his shoulder. 'And I don't intend to waste my time having to listen to any more pathetic, whining nonsense from my wife.'

'I hate him—I hate him—I *really* hate him!' Laura chanted viciously under her breath as she sorted through her case for something to wear. Thanks to the air-conditioning in the bedroom, she was at last feeling slightly cooler, but clearly none of her clothes—designed to cope with the vagaries of the English weather—were at all suitable for the steamy heat of New York. Which meant that she was obviously going to have to buy some lighter, cooler garments as soon as possible.

With a hopeless shrug of resignation she hurriedly put on a slim linen dress, which she had only thrown into her case at the last minute. Luckily it had short sleeves, and she knew that the subtle shade of pale aquamarine suited her colouring. But the material was far too heavy and the skirt much too tight for any real comfort in these conditions. Hunting through her case for some light-weight shoes, and wondering if she could get away without having to wear any stockings, she gritted her teeth as she heard her name being called from the other room.

'I'm coming—I'm coming!' she shouted back, wishing there were a key to the door as she quickly applied some light make-up.

'Ve-ry nice!' Ross drawled as she joined him, clearly

appreciating the sight before him as his hard grey eyes swept over her tall, slender figure.

'If we are going to stay here, in New York, for any length of time then I'm going to need to buy some clothes,' she told him, grimly trying to ignore the sick feeling in her stomach.

'I can't think why you should want to buy any more clothes—you look delightful in that dress.'

'It's far too hot for this climate,' she retorted flatly, her cheeks flushing as she turned away from those cynical, all-seeing eyes, beneath which she'd felt she was being mentally undressed.

Watching her, Ross asked smoothly, 'Is it going to be a problem for you, staying away from London for more than a few days?'

She shrugged. 'No. My boss is very understanding, so I'm not anticipating any problems.'

'Ah, yes. How is the admirable Mr Dunton? I must say, I had no idea that he was quite so—er—"understanding"!'

Laura was astounded, as much by the cynical scorn in his voice as by his words. Throwing all caution to the winds, she swung around to face him.

'Just what do you mean by that snide remark?' she demanded coldly. 'I'll have you know that Tim has been a very good friend to me over the past five years.'

'I just bet he has!' Ross taunted. 'After all, what could be more convenient? Working with your lover by day, and sleeping with him at night——'

'*What*?' she gasped, so shocked at what he was saying that for a moment she couldn't do anything other than stare at him with her mouth open. And then, pulling herself together, she told him through clenched teeth, 'Tim is *not* my lover!'

'He wants to marry you, doesn't he?' Ross drawled sardonically.

'Whether he does, or whether he doesn't—I can assure you that that has *nothing* to do with the quality of my work!' she hissed, barely able to remember a time when she had felt quite *so* angry. 'For your information, yes, Tim was very kind and helpful to me when I first started in the business. But I can assure you that I wouldn't have lasted five minutes in what, by any standards, is a very tricky and difficult market if I hadn't been able to cope with the work. So, if you think that I've got where I have by giving my sexual favours to Tim Dunton, or anyone else. . .'

She paused, taking a deep breath and straightening her backbone as she glared furiously at him.

'So, OK, I'm not saying that I'm the *best* commodity dealer in London. But I *do* know that I'm very good at my job. Quite apart from anything else, the competition is far too fierce for a company like McKenzie Dunton to carry any passengers. We both know what an outrageously male chauvinist pig you are, Ross—but, in case you haven't guessed, I find it *very* insulting that you should insinuate that I have somehow slept my way up to my present position!'

She had always suspected that he'd had little time for any brain power that she might possess—just as she had always known that her chief value for him had been the almost instantaneous sexual desire they had felt for each other. But to show such contempt, such disregard of what talent she might possess—*that* was what she found unforgivable.

'And let me tell you,' she swept on, powered by the hot tide of rage flowing through her veins. 'Whether I decide to marry Tim Dunton, or whether I don't, has absolutely *nothing* to do with you!'

'Oh-ho!' he laughed softly. 'There speaks the proud lioness!'

'Oh, for heaven's sake—I have enough of that nonsense from Julie back home in London,' she retorted furiously. 'Don't tell me that you believe all that nonsense too?'

Ross shrugged his broad shoulders. 'I used to think that horoscopes and all that sort of thing were sheer hocus-pocus. But now I'm not so sure,' he admitted. 'A managing director of one of my companies is a great believer in studying the star signs of applicants before employing them in the company. And when we doubled the company's turnover in one year I decided to investigate his methods.'

'It was probably just an upswing in the economy,' she snapped angrily, incensed at the way he'd succeeded in changing the subject.

'You may be right,' he agreed with a calm, maddening smile. 'However, it was interesting to discover that the sales department contained a high proportion of those born under the sign of Aries and Gemini; that the accounts department seemed to be mainly staffed by Virgos and Capricorns—all very careful with their own money, as well as the company's!'

Laura gave a scornful laugh. 'Well, if your managing director is such a hot-shot, you'd better watch out that he doesn't want to pinch *your* job!'

'Oh, no. Apparently he's a Taurean,' Ross told her blandly. 'And I am reliably informed that makes him dependable, trustworthy—and loyal unto death!'

'I couldn't care less about any of that rubbish!' she fumed. 'We were talking about *my* career, and how I'm not prepared to have you insinuate that I've slept my way to the top!'

'I did get the message,' he told her drily. 'And I can also see why you're regarded as a holy terror in the commodity-broking world.'

'*Thank you!*' she ground out savagely.

'I'd like to discuss this further with you, but I'm afraid we must leave for the hospital now,' he told her smoothly, his lips twitching with amusement at her trembling rage and fury. 'However, I'm afraid that it is *you* who are mistaken, regarding your future marriage plans,' he added, taking her arm and issuing her out of the front door.

'What do you mean?' she demanded angrily as they waited for the ancient lift to grind its way up from below.

'I mean, my dear Laura, that, since you are married to me—and I do not intend to give you a divorce—any question of your remarriage to anyone else simply doesn't arise!'

CHAPTER FIVE

LAURA sighed, lying back against the head-rest of the open sports car, closing her eyes as she relished the cool breeze rustling through her blonde hair. Ross seemed to know what he was doing—which was just as well, since it felt very weird to be travelling on what appeared to be the wrong side of the road. She turned her head slightly, opening her eyes to gaze at the firm, tanned hands clasping the wheel of the super-charged sports car that Ross had hired earlier that afternoon. Mercifully the Long Island Expressway, which Mrs Meadows had warned them might well be one long traffic jam, was proving to be relatively uncrowded. In fact, although the Hamptons were approximately eighty miles from the centre of New York, the fast sports car seemed to be making light work of the journey.

Laura could hardly wait to meet the twins again. It was two and a half years since she'd seen her god-children, Emma and Sophie, who'd last been in England with their parents on a Christmas visit, staying with Sir David and Lady Wyndham. She well remembered the tiny tots, with their white-gold, curly hair, as always getting into scrapes and having to be rescued by their mother. 'Oh, yes—I can see they're going to make me old before my time,' Liz had laughed ruefully. 'Definitely a case of double trouble!'

Laura's normally warm, full lips tightened in pain,

and she gave a heavy sigh as she recalled Liz's pale, wan face, so terribly bruised and cut when she'd visited her cousin in the hospital this morning. She'd been so relieved at the news of Liz and Owen's removal from Intensive Care that seeing the other girl's still, slight figure lying motionless on the hospital bed had been a deep and severe shock.

Warned that she could only stay for a few moments, Laura had sat down quietly in a chair beside the bed, taking her cousin's inert, pale hand and praying, as she had never prayed before, that Liz would be able to survive her ordeal. Barely conscious, Liz had nevertheless recognised Laura, and had clearly been attempting to communicate her deep distress and worry about her children.

'It's all right,' Laura had assured her quickly, instinctively knowing the reason for her cousin's distress. 'Don't worry—Ross and I will be looking after the twins. I promise you, darling, they'll be quite safe with us,' she said, speaking slowly and clearly in the hope that her cousin was able to understand.

And clearly Liz did. Because the fingers within her own warm hands ceased to flutter agitatedly, a brief smile flickering over the other girl's pale face as she seemed to drift off into a more comfortable, easy sleep.

Shaken and tearful, Laura had left the small private room, joining Ross outside in the corridor. He, too, seemed visibly affected by the brief amount of time he had been able to spend with his brother.

'Poor Owen—he seems to have broken every bone in his body,' Ross told her with a heavy sigh. And for the first time since he had so suddenly reappeared in her life

Laura saw her husband's shoulders slump, almost as if he was bearing the weight of his own brother's horrific injuries.

Without conscious thought she instinctively placed a hand on his arm. 'They're going to be all right, Ross,' she murmured softly. 'It may take time, but I'm sure they really are going to be all right.'

He nodded at her words, putting his arms about her and resting his head on her shoulder for a moment, seeking the comfort of her warm embrace. And then, with a heavy sigh that shuddered through his hard frame, he slowly released her.

'We'd better go and see the doctor,' he said heavily, taking her hand and leading her back down the corridor.

The doctor was able to tell them very little.

'It's early days yet,' he said, shaking his head. 'Both Mr and Mrs Wyndham have multiple injuries, and, although we're quite confident that they'll both pull through, we can't yet say whether there will be any permanent damage. However,' he added with a reassuring smile, 'there's no reason why, with a bit of luck, they shouldn't make a full recovery. Time will tell.'

Both she and Ross were in a very sombre, quiet mood when they left the hospital. However, as her husband so rightly pointed out, they were going to have to be upbeat and positive as far as the twins were concerned.

'I don't want those kids worrying too much about their mother and father,' he told Laura as they stood on the pavement, waiting for a cab. 'Of course, it's been an awful, terrible accident, but we've now got to concentrate on making sure that Liz and Owen get well as quickly as possible. And I'm quite sure that a major factor in their recovery is going to be knowing that their children are happy, and being well cared for.'

Laura nodded, temporarily unable to speak because of a thick lump in her throat.

'And, in order to keep the twins happy, we must make sure that we're not a picture of doom and gloom,' he continued firmly. 'It won't always be easy, but we ought to try and be as cheerful as possible.'

However, as the day had progressed Ross had grown less and less 'cheerful'. The problem, it soon transpired, was the fact that the whole of New York was intent on celebrating the national holiday. And this meant, unfortunately, that, apart from shops and restaurants, all businesses were likely to be firmly closed until the following Tuesday.

'There must be *somebody* who can mend this damn air-conditioning,' Ross swore violently after his umpteenth failure to contact an electrical repair man. 'The superintendent of this building appears to be a broken reed, and unless I spend the next twenty-four hours on the telephone it looks as though we are plumb out of luck,' he added, throwing the phone book down in disgust.

'It's stifling in here—we'll have to do something before we bring the twins back to this apartment,' Laura agreed. 'And I really am going to need some help. I mean. . . I'm anxious to do what I can, but I don't know the first thing about looking after children. I haven't a clue what food they ought to eat, for instance.'

Ross snorted with exasperation. 'Oh, come on—there can't be anything to it. You are a woman, after all.'

Laura gave a hollow laugh. 'I'm not denying my gender,' she told him wryly. 'Unfortunately, being female doesn't necessarily mean that I instinctively know how to behave as a mother. For instance—do *you* know how to change a baby's nappy?'

'No, of course I don't!' he snapped.

'Well, unfortunately—surprise, surprise—neither do I!'

They stared glumly at each other for a few moments, before Laura shrugged. 'Of course, the twins are well past the nappy stage—or I imagine they must be—and, since I've promised Liz that I'll look after them, you can be sure that I'll do what I can.'

'I know you will,' he agreed quietly.

'However, in the meantime I'm going to be badly in need of some professional help,' Laura told him urgently. 'Of course,' she added slyly, 'there's no reason why you couldn't look after the children. Quite frankly, I've always been a great believer in equal opportunities!'

A look of horror flickered across his face. 'OK—OK, you've made your point,' he said with a short bark of rueful laughter.

Trying to arrange a temporary nanny proved to be as useless as their hunt for an electrician. All the agencies they contacted, despite being willing to help, all reported that their staff were fully booked over the holiday. However, a phone call from Mrs Meadows seemed to offer a temporary solution to their problem. Very kindly, Carole and Ben Meadows invited them to come and stay over the weekend.

'It's just so gorgeous out here,' Carole Meadows enthused over the phone. 'And the kids are all having such fun together, building sand-castles and swimming in the sea. So why don't you all take a break from the city? We'd sure love to put you up for a few days.'

'That's an offer we can't refuse!' Ross agreed gratefully, arranging to hire a car and drive out to the Hampton's later on that afternoon.

Since leaving the hospital Laura had felt much more in accord with Ross, united as they both were by their deep concern for the twins and their parents. Unfortunately, the fragile harmony between them was soon broken when she found herself arguing furiously with him in the dress department of Bloomingdales.

Due to her unexpected and hasty departure from England, Laura found that she'd left her charge cards behind in her apartment. And, since the banks were now firmly closed until the end of the holiday, and she only had a small amount of currency in her purse, she had no way of being able to buy any new, cooler dresses. Not, that was, without the help of her husband.

'I don't see the problem,' Ross told her with a shrug. 'I've got plenty of cash—and charge cards, too, if it comes to that,' he added, firmly grasping her arm and marching her into the large department store.

Wishing she'd kept her mouth shut and never mentioned her need of some new clothes, Laura found herself being dragged, willy-nilly, towards the lifts. Minutes later Ross was calling for the manageress of the designer-wear department—and imperiously stating his requirements.

'I'm perfectly capable of choosing my own dresses!' she hissed angrily. But all to no avail as, grumbling furiously under her breath, she found herself being led away to a changing-room.

Earning a very large salary, Laura was quite used to buying expensive clothes—primarily, of course, smart and severely cut suits to wear at work. However, she now found herself losing touch with all reality as Ross, obviously frustrated in his efforts to sort out their air-conditioning and nanny problems, proceeded to spend a small fortune on his wife.

It was when he insisted on hauling her off to the sports-wear department that Laura made a really determined effort to bring him to his senses.

'There's no way I'm going to be able to wear all these outfits,' she protested loudly as he selected one ravishingly pretty swimsuit after another. 'We're only going away for a *weekend*, for heaven's sake! And, in any case, I never wear a bikini,' she added firmly.

But Ross took no notice. 'They'll come in useful when you go abroad on holiday,' he told her firmly. 'They'd be perfect for the Caribbean, for instance.'

'But I don't go abroad on holiday—and I've never *been* to the Caribbean,' she wailed helplessly as he added yet another gorgeous outfit to the huge pile he'd already chosen.

'Well, it's time you did. "All work and no play has made Laura a very dull girl,"' he misquoted in a thoroughly hateful, sanctimonious voice which immediately raised her hackles.

'*Dull*. . .?' she cried in a shrill voice, oblivious of the shocked expression on the sales girl's face as she rounded angrily on her husband. 'I've just about had you—in spades! How dare you say that I'm dull?' she stormed, the accumulations of the day taking their toll as she swung at him with her handbag.

Unfortunately she'd missed. And equally unfortunately Ross's only response had been a low, taunting laugh before ruthlessly pulling her furiously angry figure into his arms. Ignoring her frantic efforts to break free, he'd tossed his charge card down on to the counter. Requesting the sales girl to make up the bill, he'd proceeded to lower his dark head, his arms closing about her like steel bands as he'd possessed Laura's lips in a long, slow and devastating kiss.

Even now, with the sports car scorching along the expressway, and the breeze cooling her flushed cheeks, Laura still felt almost sick with embarrassment. That kiss, which had left her feeling totally shattered, had been clearly meant more as a punishment than a pleasure. And when Ross had proceeded to tell all the interested spectators—of which there had been many— that he and Laura were on their second honeymoon. . .she'd almost exploded with loathing of the man who was now so clearly dominating her life.

Glancing through her eyelashes at his stern features, the tanned arrogance of his hawk-like profile as he concentrated on the road before him, Laura clasped her shaking hands tightly together in her lap. Wearing a pair of slim, immaculately cut navy blue trousers, topped by a short-sleeved shirt of the same colour, open at the neck to display the strong column of his throat, Ross's powerful frame exuded such an air of raw, vibrant masculinity that she felt suddenly breathless, almost unable to prevent her knees from trembling violently beneath the skirt of her pale aquamarine dress.

'I think it's about time that you stopped sulking,' Ross drawled coolly.

'I'm *not* sulking!' she snapped.

He laughed. 'Oh, yes, you are!'

Thoroughly incensed, she glared at his handsome face. But, when he turned and gave her a warm, infectious grin, she found it difficult not to smile back at him.

'Well. . .well, maybe I *was* sulking—just a little bit,' she added quickly as he gave a low rumble of laughter. 'But, you must admit, I did have a lot to put up with today.'

'What about me?' he demanded. 'I can't think of any other woman of my acquaintance who would kick up such a fuss just because a man wanted to buy her some new clothes. Most of the girls I know——'

'And, you know so many, of course!' she added caustically.

He gave a slight shrug of his shoulders. 'I've met quite a few during the past five years,' he agreed smoothly.

'I just bet you have!' she ground out, echoing the words he had used about her relationship with Tim Dunton earlier this morning.

'*Touché*!'

The amusement in his voice as he acknowledged her quick, telling point merely added fuel to the flames of her simmering anger.

'And it isn't just women and girls in the plural, is it?' she queried sourly. 'Let us not forget *dear* Marissa. . .!'

Ross frowned at the strong note of venom in her voice. 'Marissa?' he queried blankly. 'I can't think why you appear to be so preoccupied with that girl.'

'Oh, can't you?' Laura gave a carelessly high-pitched laugh, which even to her own ears sounded remarkably unconvincing. She would have continued to attack him further, but, even as she opened her mouth to tell him *exactly* what she thought of philandering, two-timing men who played around with their office staff, she heard Ross swearing violently under his breath.

'I've had quite enough of this nonsense,' he growled impatiently. 'Irrespective of how we feel about each other, we must now put such emotions aside, and concentrate on the only really important issues. We're just a few miles away from the Meadowses' place,' he added, reaching forward to extract a map from the glove compartment, and tossing it on to her lap. 'I want you, first of all, to direct me through Quogue. And while you're doing that, Laura,' he added with low menace, 'I suggest that you try and pull yourself together. Because, by the time we reach the house where the twins are staying, I expect you to be in a friendly, pleasant state of mind. *Do I make myself clear?*' he added threateningly.

'As daylight,' she snapped, before giving a heavy sigh as she realised that, yet again, the horrid man had succeeded in putting her in the wrong.

Because, of course, she couldn't argue with the sense that lay behind his harsh words. For the twins' sakes, she *must* put aside all her antagonistic feelings, the deep frustration she felt at having to coexist, cheek by jowl, with a man she fervently hoped would soon be her *ex*-husband. Although even the thought of a quick divorce from this man, when Liz and Owen had returned to full health, didn't seem to lift her spirits, somehow. But, for Emma's and Sophie's sakes, she really must try to do her best.

Carole Meadows was charming and welcoming, and

within five minutes of their arrival Laura could feel many of the day's traumas slipping off her tired shoulders.

'You poor girl!' Carole told her, putting a plump, comforting arm about her as she led Laura into the large ranch-style house. 'What a *terrible* time you must have had—having to fly all this way to the States, and then to see poor, darling Liz and Owen when they're so terribly, terribly ill. It just breaks my heart, honey, to think of your poor, dear cousin in such pain,' the other woman murmured sympathetically, her eyes glistening with tears as she begged Laura to sit down and make herself comfortable.

Feeling almost overwhelmed by their hostess's kind welcome, Laura sank down into a wide, soft couch, looking about her as Carole bustled off to fetch a cool drink.

When she'd learned that Ben and Carole Meadows were staying at their beach-front cottage Laura had somehow assumed that it would be a very small, modest building. However, by no stretch of the imagination would she have ever referred to this magnificent house as a 'cottage'.

Even here, amid the soft, cooling sea breezes, she noticed that the house appeared to be centrally air-conditioned. But, as she gazed around at the chintz sofas, and the French-provincial-style velvet-upholstered dining-room chairs—which she could see through a far open doorway—it occurred to Laura that maybe it was the only way to preserve such sumptuous furnishings on a shoreline likely to be damp and salty in the latter part of the year, while, outside the large windows, she could see automatic sprinklers drenching the fine green lawns that ran down to the beach.

Some cottage! she thought, quickly repressing a giggle at her own mistaken ideas as Ross and Ben Meadows entered the room.

'I thought we'd better just have a quiet word together before we go down and see the kids on the beach,' Ben was saying as Carole bustled back into the room, carrying a tray laden with plates of cakes and biscuits.

'Hey—where are your manners?' Carole asked her husband with a slight laugh. 'I guess these folk must be dying for a cool drink and some cookies, right?' She grinned at Laura.

'Yes, that's very welcome,' she agreed, quietly sipping a tall glass of orange as Ben explained to both her and Ross exactly what they'd told the twins so far.

'So, as you can see,' he concluded with a shrug, 'we've kept things pretty light. The kids know that their parents have been in a car crash, of course. But we've made sure that they don't realise the extent of the injuries. There will be plenty of time for you to have to cope with that when they return to the city and visit Liz and Owen in hospital.'

Ross nodded. 'That sounds just about the right approach to me,' he agreed. 'It's remarkably kind of you to put us up like this, and we're both very grateful.' He smiled down at Carole, the pretty, plump woman flushing beneath the warmth in his grey eyes.

'Hey, you folks, it was the very least we could do. And we're insisting that you stay here just as long as you like,' she told them. 'Certainly, there's no point in you going back to New York, before Tuesday at the earliest. Right, Ben?'

Her husband nodded vigorously. 'Absolutely right. By the way,' he added, turning to Ross, 'don't you worry your head about the financial position of your brother and his wife. As Owen's lawyer, I can promise you that I'm going to sue the socks off the drunken driver who caused that terrible accident,' he vowed firmly.

Their reunion with the twins—who'd been playing on the beach with the Meadowes's little girl, Kerry-Jane—was an almost heartbreaking occasion. A deep lump seemed to fill Laura'a throat as the little blonde girls clung to her for some minutes.

'It's all right, darlings. There's no need to worry,' she told them softly. 'Uncle Ross and I have been to see your mummy and daddy—and they are going to be just fine.'

'Really and truly?' Emma—or was it Sophie?—demanded urgently.

'Really and truly,' Laura told them both firmly, heedless of her smart dress and shoes as she knelt on the damp sand, her arms placed warmly about their two anxious figures. 'Of course, they're feeling very sore at the moment,' she added carefully. 'But they *are* going to get well. In fact, I know that Mummy is looking forward to seeing you both just as soon as we get back to New York after the holiday.'

Glancing up, she caught Ross's nod and warm smile of approval at the efforts she was making to reassure Emma and Sophie about their parents' condition. Surprised to find herself so ridiculously pleased by his approbation, she was quickly distracted as Sophie—or was it Emma?—asked, 'You and Uncle Ross aren't going to leave us, are you? I mean. . .'

'She means,' the other twin chimed in, 'you are going to stay with us until Mummy and Daddy come out of the hos-hospital?' she asked, finding difficulty in coping with the long word.

'Of course we are,' Ross told them, bending down to pick up one twin and then the other. The little girls squealed with delight as he swung them round in a circle, before setting them back gently on to the sand.

'Now, see here, you children,' he told the twins and Kerry-Jane with mock sternness, 'I don't think much of those sand-castles.' He pointed towards the rather lumpy piles of sand near the water's edge. 'Aunt Laura and I are going to get out of these stuffy city clothes—and put on something more comfortable. In the meantime, I want you all to try and build me a decent-sized castle, right?'

'He sure has a good touch with those kids, doesn't he?' Carole laughed as she and Laura followed the two men back towards the house.

'Yes. . .yes, he does,' Laura agreed thoughtfully, surprised at Ross's instinctive, natural way with the young children.

'He'd make a marvellous father,' Carole enthused. 'And I guess it won't be too long before you both have some kids of your own,' she added, giving the beautiful blonde girl a friendly dig in the ribs.

'What. . .?' Laura turned to look at the other woman in astonishment. The Meadowses were obviously good friends of Liz and Owen. So surely they must know about the situation between Ross and herself?

Carole gazed at her with concern. 'Oh, dear, I hope I haven't said the wrong thing? I didn't realise that you might not—er—be able to have any babies. . .' she added with an unhappy sigh, clearly wishing that she'd kept her mouth shut.

'Oh, no,' Laura hastened to reassure her. 'It isn't that. I'm sure when the time comes. . . I mean, as far as I know, there's no reason why. . .' Her voice trailed away as she realised, from the other woman's beaming smile of relief, that she'd inadvertently given her hostess *quite* the wrong impression.

Carole's next words confirmed it. 'I'm so glad— because you'd obviously make a marvellous mother,' she said enthusiastically.

And then, just as Laura was opening her mouth to explain exactly why motherhood wasn't an item on her agenda, she was dumbfounded when Carole added, in a matter-of-fact voice, 'Leo ladies may be stylish and glamorous, but they also make great wives and mothers.'

'How did you guess. . .? I mean. . .' Laura shook her head in disbelief. Why was it that everyone she'd met lately seemed to be obsessed with star signs?

Carole laughed. 'Didn't Liz tell you that I've written some books on the subject?'

'No, I'm afraid she didn't,' Laura confessed.

'Well—it's no big deal,' the other woman assured her with a grin. 'I tend to keep quiet about it—otherwise most of the women I know would want me to draw up their horoscope! But I knew straight away that you and that handsome husband of yours just *had* to be Leos!'

'Yes—er—you're right,' Laura admitted.

'Well, as marriages go, it certainly isn't dull! But

there's no doubt, honey,' the other woman added with a warm smile, 'that when two Leos really get it together it can be *the* most romantic marriage of all time. And it looks to me as if you two lovely people were just *made* for each other!'

As they left the beach and walked back across the green lawn Laura didn't have the opportunity to shatter Carole's totally incorrect, if highly romantic illusions as the other woman called out to Ross. While Ben went to get their luggage she led her guests over to a small building, separated from the main house by a large garage complex.

'This is our little guest cottage,' she announced as they mounted some steps on to a wide, spacious veranda which ran the length of the property. 'Ben and I were sure that you must still be feeling jet lagged. We reckon this if far enough away from the main house to make sure that you get some real peace and quiet.'

'It's. . .it's simply lovely,' Laura murmured as Carole showed them around the cottage. 'But what about Emma and Sophie. . .?'

Carole turned her head and gave her a broad smile. 'My Kerry-Jane and the twins are happily sharing the nursery suite in the main house. They just love it there— Ben has fixed up a really cute play-room, and they can make all the noise they want without disturbing anyone. So you folks can just relax, and have a nice quiet time.'

As they entered the bedroom Laura stared in consternation at the huge, wide bed, which practically filled what appeared to be the only bedroom in the cottage. 'Er—I'm afraid that——' she began. But before she could say anything further Ross—who had remained silent so far—took a quick step forward and gathered her into his arms.

Gasping with surprise at the suddenness of his action, she didn't have the opportunity to say anything when—just as in Bloomingdales—he possessed her lips in a firm and determined kiss.

Slowly raising his head, he gazed over the shattered, bemused figure in his arms, to give Carole a beaming smile. 'We've both been working so hard that this break has given us the opportunity for a second honeymoon,' he told her smoothly. 'So obviously this guest cottage of yours is going to be just perfect.'

Laura stared up at Ross in stupefied amazement. His talents were obviously being wasted in business. Anyone who could put on such an outrageous act—*and* get away with it—quite clearly ought to have been on the stage!

And then, as Carole Meadows wiped a tear from her eye, murmuring, 'Oh, isn't that just *so* romantic?' Laura realised that the dreadful man had somehow managed to outmanoeuvre her once again.

CHAPTER SIX

BOILING with rage, yet forced to keep a fixed smile on her face while Carole Meadows continued showing them around the small guest cottage, Laura could barely contain her fury. Interesting and indeed impressive as it might have been to learn that the drinking water was purified through an electric purifier, and that the shower contained a tension-soothing massage attachment, everything paled into insignificance beside her over-whelming desire to give her loathsome husband's shins a *very* painful kick!

Eventually, their tour of inspection at an end, Carole turned to leave.

'Now, I want you both to just relax and take it easy,' she told them with a warm smile. 'We'll be having a quiet family supper at around seven o'clock, and you'll be able to tuck the twins up in bed after that, OK?' she added, brushing away their thanks as she bustled off towards the large ranch house.

Waiting impatiently until their hostess had disappeared from sight, Laura was just opening her mouth to give vent to her intense anger, when she was frustrated yet again by the arrival of Ben, carrying their suitcases.

'I figured you'd want to get out of those city clothes straight away,' he told them with a grin. 'I hope Carole has explained how everything works?'

'Yes, indeed she has, and we're very grateful,' Ross

95

told him. 'In fact, both my wife and I are quite overcome by all your kindness.'

Ben's cheeks reddened slightly at the warm, deeply sincere note in Ross's voice. 'Think nothing of it. We're just anxious to do what we can. Now, I expect you'll both want to have a nice cold shower—so I'll leave you to get on with it,' he added, giving them another of his slow, friendly smiles before he, too, made his way back to the larger house.

In the silence following his departure Laura glared at her husband. Thanks to the various interruptions, she was finding it difficult to maintain the high temperature of her initial furious reaction to his kiss. In fact, if it hadn't been an important point of principle not to let the damn impertinent man get away with his nauseating behaviour, she'd have let the whole thing drop. Because, quite honestly, she was feeling absolutely worn out. Maybe she was still suffering from jet lag or, possibly, from the deeply upsetting and traumatic visit to the hospital this morning. However, whatever the reason, she suddenly realised that she was feeling far too tired and exhausted to pick yet another fight with Ross.

As the long silence lengthened between them Laura desperately tried to find some adequate words to express her disgust at his actions. After all, even if she could hardly bear to face another row, she was going to have to put a stop to all this nonsense, and as soon as possible.

'I quite agree with you.'

'What. . .?' Laura frowned as Ross's deep voice cut into her thoughts.

He shrugged his shoulders, before walking over to the small refrigerator set in a corner of the living-room. 'I

Four Irresistible *Temptations* FREE!

PLUS A MYSTERY GIFT

Temptations offer you all the age-old passion and tenderness of romance, now experienced through very contemporary relationships.

And to introduce to you this powerful and highly charged series, we'll send you **four Temptation romances** absolutely **FREE** when you complete and return this card.

We're so confident that you'll enjoy Temptations that we'll also reserve a subscription to our Reader Service, for you; which means that you'll enjoy...

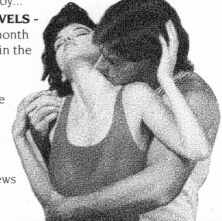

🔖 **FOUR BRAND NEW NOVELS -** sent direct to you each month (before they're available in the shops).

🔖 **FREE POSTAGE AND PACKING -** we pay all the extras.

🔖 **FREE MONTHLY NEWSLETTER -** packed with special offers, competitions, authors news and much more...

CLAIM THESE GIFTS OVERLEAF

Free Books Certificate

A Free Gift

Return this card now and we'll send you this cuddly Teddy Bear absolutely FREE together with....

A Mystery Gift

We all love mysteries, so as well as the FREE Teddy Bear there's an intriguing FREE gift specially for you.

YES! Please send me **four FREE Temptations** together with my **FREE gifts**. Please also reserve a special Reader Service subscription for me. If I decide to subscribe, I will receive four Temptation romances each month for just £7.00 postage and packing free. If I decide not to subscribe, I shall write to you within 10 days. The free books and gifts are mine to keep in any case. **I understood that I am under no obligation whatsoever**. I may cancel or suspend my subscription at any time simply by writing to you. I am over 18 years of age.

7A2T

MS/MRS/MISS/MR _____

ADDRESS _____

POSTCODE _____ SIGNATURE _____

was just attempting to prevent a severe loss of temper on your part,' he drawled smoothly, removing a cold bottle of wine from the fridge. 'So, how about if I agree that I'm unprincipled, absolutely despicable, and thoroughly reprehensible—or, indeed, any other term of abuse you might care to use? By the way, can you see a corkscrew anywhere?' he continued in exactly the same mild tone of voice.

'No, I can't!' she snapped, glowering over at his tall figure. She hadn't wanted another argument, but perversely she was now filled with deep resentment at the way he was hijacking her right to tear him to pieces.

'It's all right, I don't need one. This bottle seems to have a plastic stopper,' he murmured as he filled two glasses. 'Here—drink this and you'll soon feel a great deal better,' he added, walking across the room towards her. 'And, for goodness' sake, Laura, stop standing there like Joan of Arc about to be burnt at the stake!'

'Well, you must admit——' she began as he handed her a glass.

He clicked his teeth impatiently. 'I'll admit anything you like—but why don't you start using your brains for a change?' he told her roughly. 'We've already decided to bury our differences and concentrate on the welfare of Emma and Sophie—right?'

As she gave a brief nod he continued, 'The Meadowses have been incredibly kind, and are obviously doing what they can to make us feel welcome. Unfortunately, you have a tendency to allow your obviously muddled, rather juvenile feelings about myself to cloud your judgement.'

Wincing at the hard, grating note in his voice, Laura

stared down at her glass for a moment. 'But don't you see——?'

'I see a lot more than you've ever given me credit for!' he retorted curtly. 'And no, I don't know why Liz and Owen didn't tell their friends about the temporary separation between us,' he added, accurately reading her mind.

'What do you mean, "temporary"?' She gave a shrill laugh. 'I would have said our separation was about as permanent as you can get!'

'Then you'd be quite wrong!' he said forcefully, ignoring her rising tide of protest as he continued, 'I want it clearly understood—*once and for all*—that, as far as the outside world is concerned, you and I are still happily married. A situation which will continue until such time as my brother and his wife have fully recovered from their injuries.'

'But. . .but it might be ages before they are really well.' She looked at him, aghast. 'You can't possibly expect me to carry on this sort of charade—not for that length of time?'

'That's *exactly* what I expect!' He stared menacingly down at her. 'You gave me your word, Laura, that you would look after the twins to the very best of your ability.'

'Yes, I did, but——'

'They obviously need a happy home environment—and, as far as I'm concerned, that's exactly what they are going to get,' he continued remorselessly, completely ignoring her interjection. 'Of course, if you've now decided that you aren't prepared to look after Emma and Sophie, if you don't care about their future welfare or happiness, then I suggest you'd better catch the next plane back to England.'

'That's not fair!' she protested quickly. 'You *know* that I'll do anything for the children. I've already said that I would.'

'If you really mean what you say, then the solution is obvious: you and I must simply bury our differences for the time being. It surely isn't too much to ask—not if it's going to make two little girls happy and contented?'

'Don't think that I don't know when I'm being blackmailed—because I do!' she told him bitterly, before giving a heavy sigh. 'However, I can see that I'm in a no-win situation. Although how the two of us sharing a bed is going to make the twins more happy and contented is quite beyond me,' she muttered grimly, adding quickly as he took a threatening step towards her, 'OK— OK, I'll go along with this mad charade. But if you lay one finger on me I'll. . . I'll. . .'

'You'll what?' he drawled sardonically, before putting down his glass and carrying their suitcases through into the bedroom. 'Even a blind man could see that I hold all the cards in this situation,' he told her flatly as she trailed slowly and miserably into the room behind him. 'So I suggest that you start concentrating on playing the part of a loving and dutiful wife.'

You'll be lucky! Laura wanted to scream at him, aware of a tension headache beginning to grip her head in a vice as the stress of the day's events began to take their toll. But he was right. Ross did hold all the cards, she acknowledged bitterly. He had so manipulated the situation that if she wanted to do what she could for the twins she had no alternative but to agree to his terms.

Later that night Laura lay in bed, staring at the thin, shadowy shafts of moonlight filtering through the louvred window. Goodness knows where Ross had got to, but he wasn't—thankfully—lying here beside her tense, nervous body.

Following the row between them, she had been frankly dreading the evening which had lain ahead. However, and probably thanks to Carole Meadows' warm, engaging personality, it had proved to be much easier than she could have imagined. And when she had helped Carole to put Emma and Sophie to bed she hadn't been able to prevent tears coming to her eyes while she had listened to them solemnly saying their prayers.

It was then Laura had realised that, however difficult it might be, she would make any sacrifice in order for the twins to be as happy and contented as possible. So, as much as it went against the grain, she knew she had no alternative but to fit in with Ross's plans.

Ross! Where was the damn man? Not that she wanted him here in bed with her, of course, she told herself quickly. But if they were supposed to be keeping up the fiction about being happily married—a second honeymoon, indeed!—then it was going to look a bit odd, if not downright peculiar, if he didn't spend his nights here in the cottage.

However, as the minutes ticked away, and she grew gradually more sleepy, some of the tension began leaving her body. For almost the first time since his reappearance in her life Laura found herself wondering whether she and Ross could have done anything to save their marriage all those years ago.

Of course, the sad truth behind the break-up of many young couples' marriages was just that—they'd been too young. So maybe the relationship between her and Ross had never really stood a chance. Although he was nine years older than her, her youth and immaturity must, she realised, have played quite a large part. She'd been devastated by her mother's sudden illness and totally unexpected death. So would she really have been any less affected if it had happened to her now, at the age of twenty-five?

However, she doubted whether she would be able to cope—even now—with Ross's formidable mother. The older woman hadn't bothered to hide her dismay at what she had seen as the loss of her precious older son. The equally obvious fact that she had clearly felt he'd married well beneath him—and into a family of which she had already disapproved—was something that Laura hadn't known how to deal with. Baffled by the elderly woman's total animosity and unreasonable behaviour, she had at first responded by being anxiously deferential—abjectly agreeing to every outrageous demand on her husband's precious time, despite not seeing very much of him herself. And then, when that clearly hadn't worked, Laura had found herself lapsing into a sullen, resentful attitude, defiantly refusing to have anything to do with the beastly old woman.

Neither attitude had been, of course, the right way to tackle the problem. Nowadays, with a far more sophisticated outlook on life, Laura hoped that she would be able to deal with the indomitable woman in a calm and reasoned manner.

Similarly, she was almost sure that she would be far more understanding of Ross's total drive and absorption in his business. After working for some years in the hectic, fast-moving world of City finance, she now understood far more clearly the pressures and compulsive need to succeed that characterised most leading businessmen. Knowing something of the stresses and strains involved, she would have been able to share more fully in his ever-increasing involvement and total absorption with the Wyndham International Banking Corporation.

Engaged in rapidly expanding the size of the business, which he had taken over from his father, Ross had had little or no time for his young wife or her problems. And thus, when her father's ghastly illness had first been diagnosed, and had then continued on its remorseless path, she'd only discovered—when it was far too late—that she and Ross had been growing steadily and disastrously apart.

Unfortunately Laura was almost sure that even *now*, and despite every ounce of sophistication at her command, she *still* wouldn't be able to cope with the intrusion of Marissa Kenton into her husband's life.

Not realising what had been going on, she'd failed to understand why he'd had to spend so many nights in the penthouse suite of his office. She hadn't accepted then—and she was pretty certain that she wouldn't do so now—his dismissive claim that it was solely due to the pressure of business. Of course, Ross's inability to telephone, or feel the need to apologise or explain his frequent absences, hadn't helped matters. And when Laura had protested, as she frequently had, he had merely pointed out with brutal logic, 'You knew I was a businessman when you married me, Laura. It's about time that you grew up and realised that I cannot possibly be dancing attendance on you every five minutes.'

And maybe she wouldn't have been expecting him to 'dance attendance' on her if she hadn't soon discovered that he'd been spending so much time with his personal assistant! Marissa, a tall cool girl with hair as dark as night, had been not only obviously very clever, but also—alas—very beautiful.

Even after all these years, Laura knew that it would have taken a paragon of virtue not to feel viciously jealous of the svelte, sophisticated woman who had seemed to spend far more time with her husband than she did. And, to rub further salt into her wounds, Marissa had treated the younger girl with a cool, obvious contempt that had quickly begun to strip away Laura's small store of self-confidence. As the weeks had gone by the other girl had dropped more and more blatant hints about the fact that she was having an affair with her employer.

Increasingly it had seemed that the only time Laura saw Ross was when he slid into bed at night, and would once again become the demanding and passionate lover she had married. But even that last saving grace of their relationship had begun to collapse when she had had to spend so much of her time down in Devon, looking after her father and his chaotic affairs.

Following weeks of arguments, which had gradually

become more and more bitter, the crunch when it came had been swift and brutal.

'I'm sorry about your father,' Ross had told her one morning before leaving for work. 'I realise that he has considerable problems. But I don't consider that those problems should have to be shouldered by you, and you alone. You are *my* wife,' he'd added firmly, picking up his briefcase and preparing to leave the apartment. 'I'm flying to Australia next week, and I expect you to accompany me. Not only am I *not* prepared to have a semi-detached marriage, but I'm convinced that if you *really* cared for me you would have no hesitation about placing my interests first,' had been his parting shot as he had left the apartment, slamming the front door loudly behind him.

Stiff with pride—which she was *now* sick and tired of being told was a Leo trait—and buoyed up by the certain knowledge that it would have been morally indefensible for her to desert her father, Laura had taken some weeks to realise that there must surely have been another way for them to solve their problems. Maybe, for instance, she could sell her father's estate to pay his debts, and then she could take him with her to Australia? After all, there must have been many comfortable nursing homes in Sydney where her father, who had then been having difficulty in telling even night from day, would have received the sort of care and attention which he had needed.

But when she had tried to contact Ross some weeks after his departure she had had no idea how to get in touch with him. The only route had lain through Marissa Kenton, who had still been firmly ensconced in the London office. And so, although she had hated having to do it, Laura had forced herself to write a long letter to Ross, saying how very much she loved and missed him—and couldn't they still try to salvage something from the wreck of their marriage?

She had never, of course, received even a bare acknowledgement from her husband. And when she'd got the same blank response to two further letters she'd sent him, Laura had sorrowfully realised that her marriage was indeed at an end. And it had been little comfort to realise—since he clearly couldn't be bothered to even make the effort to get in touch with her—that her marriage had obviously been a disastrous mistake from the very beginning.

In fact, for the first year or two she'd expected to hear from him, asking for a divorce so that he could marry Marissa, who had, apparently, followed him to Sydney. But his continuing silence had brought her to the conclusion that he was content, with both his semi-bachelor life and his affair with his personal assistant, an affair he was still obviously continuing, she thought grimly, recalling the phone call he'd received from his 'personal assistant' in Liz's apartment earlier this morning.

Maybe that was the basic problem, she told herself wearily as she now stared blindly up at the ceiling. Maybe Ross should never had got married in the first place. Maybe he'd bitterly regretted the impulse that had led him to marry such a young girl—possibly the only rash decision of his well-ordered life. After all, he'd always clearly preferred the ruthless cut and thrust of the business world to that of marriage and domesticity—

his freedom to that of commitment. And she could hardly blame him after the disaster of their own brief marriage, Laura now thought wryly. Because she herself had subsequently been extremely wary of any emotional entanglements. Fond as she was of Tim Dunton, she had repeatedly and steadfastly refused all his proposals of marriage.

Although, now she came to think about it, maybe such caution had been a grave mistake. So, OK, she didn't want to marry Tim—but if she *had* married him she wouldn't now be forced into playing the part of Ross's loving and dutiful wife. Loving. . .? That's a laugh! she thought miserably, trying hard not to listen to the quiet voice at the back of her head which seemed to be suggesting that she might, even after all this time, still be in love with her husband.

Giving herself a good talking to, and ruthlessly ignoring those silly, pathetic yearnings still buried deep in her subconscious, had always worked in the past. So why should she now be having such difficulty, finding all her old arguments so unconvincing? A question which remained obstinately hovering in her mind as she slowly slipped into a deep sleep.

She was awoken, what seemed only minutes later, by a heavy weight suddenly landing on her chest. Coughing and spluttering as she gasped for air, Laura was jerked into consciousness by the sound of a high-pitched giggle and the feel of a wet kiss on her cheek.

'Good morning, Aunt Laura,' a small voice rang out. 'It's a *lovely* day!'

Inching one eyelid open, Laura saw that Sophie—or was it Emma?—was now happily bouncing up and down on the mattress beside her. And then, opening the other eye, she saw that the other little girl, Emma—or was it Sophie?—had leaped on to the bed to join her sister.

'We're going to have to do something—because I simply can't tell you two imps of mischief apart,' Laura muttered, groaning as she levered herself up against the pillows. Brushing a shaky, tired hand through her tangled blonde hair, she squinted down at the watch on her wrist.

'Oh, my God—I don't believe it! It's only seven o'clock!' she moaned.

'Daddy always said it was rude to swear like that,' one of the twins informed her, giving her pretty blonde aunt a wide, beaming grin.

'Your daddy was quite right.'

The unexpected sound of the deep voice suddenly coming from somewhere beside her made Laura almost jump out of her skin. Turning her head, she met a slow, sleepy smile from Ross as he, too, raised himself to a sitting position against the pillows.

'Aren't you pleased that we've come over to wake you up?' one of the twins asked.

'Oh, yes, absolutely—er—thrilled to bits,' Laura croaked, well aware of the low rumble of laughter from the man beside her.

Doing her best to ignore the sight of his bare torso, it was some moments before she recalled the fact that Ross had never worn any pyjamas. As she realised that he must be completely and utterly naked there seemed nothing she could do to stop a deep tide of crimson from rising up over her cheeks.

'Are you feeling all right?' one of the twins asked, peering at her aunt in concern.

'Oh, yes, I'm. . . I'm fine,' Laura mumbled, so used to silence first thing in the morning that she was finding it incredibly difficult to carry on any form of conversation. 'Which one of you is Emma?' she asked sleepily. The twins really were so identical that it was virtually impossible to tell them apart.

'It's easy to tell Emma—'cos she's got a mole on her bottom!' Sophie giggled.

'Er—I think I'm going to need something a bit easier to spot than that.' Laura's smile turned into a wide yawn. 'Isn't there any other way we can tell the difference?'

'Well, Sophie's got a slight chip off her front tooth,' the other girl said, reaching forward to pull up her twin's lip. 'That's where she fell down on the sidewalk, and cried and cried and cried. . .'

'No, I didn't!'

'Oh, yes, you did!'

And then, as one of the children seized a pillow, and began batting the other one over the head, the second girl quickly retaliated. Almost before Laura could blink her eyes a vigorous pillow-fight seemed to be taking place as the two small girls charged back and forth across the bed, screaming with laughter when they managed to score a hit.

'Are all kids like this?' she asked Ross in a low voice.

He grinned. 'Oh, yes—I should think so. Owen and I used to have regular pillow-fights. What about you and Liz?'

'I don't honestly remember. . .' She closed her eyes,

leaning back against her remaining pillow as she tried to recall that aspect of her childhood. A few moments later when she opened her eyes she was startled to find her vision filled by the tanned shoulders of Ross as he leaned over her prone body.

'What do you think you're doing. . .?' she gasped, becoming breathlessly aware of a deep, pounding throb in the pit of her stomach. The strange excitement seemed to spread, racing through her veins like a rushing tide as he lowered his dark head towards her. Her frantic attempts to push away those wide shoulders proved to be of no avail, and there was nothing she could do to prevent his mouth gently brushing her lips.

'I know the twins used to visit their parents early in the morning—which is *why* we have to share a bed,' he breathed softly. But it took her some moments to understand exactly what he was saying, her senses reeling at the warmth of the hard naked chest pressed so closely to her soft breasts, her nostrils savouring the erotic, musky scent of his skin.

'Daddy often kisses Mummy,' a high treble voice announced as one of the twins bounced across the bed, viewing with considerable interest the two grown-ups lying so closely together. 'Do you like kissing Aunt Laura?' the little girl asked her uncle.

Ross's deep chuckle of laughter effectively masked Laura's low groan of embarrassment. Lifting his head, he turned to grin at the little girl. 'Yes, I most certainly do!' he told her before turning back to stare down at the flushed features of his wife.

The light, mocking note in his voice was acutely disturbing, as was the gleam in those deeply hooded granite-grey eyes as they studied her so intently. And then, almost as if he had received some secret signal, he gave a slight nod of his head, grinning sardonically down at her for a moment before rolling off her body and gathering one of the twins up in his arms.

'I think it would be a good idea if we all had a swim before breakfast, don't you?' he said, the announcement seized upon with alacrity by the two little girls who, once again, began jumping up and down on the mattress as if it were a trampoline.

'That's enough of that,' Ross told them firmly as he threw aside the sheets, revealing the fact that he was wearing a pair of boxer shorts. 'I didn't want to shock the girls—or you, for that matter,' he murmured drily, his eyes glinting with amusement at her flustered, hastily murmured denial.

'I'm not the slightest bit interested in you—or what you wear!' she hissed at him beneath the sound of the children's laughter as they jumped off the bed, and scampered about the room.

He gave another low, maddening laugh, his tall figure looming menacingly over her trembling body. 'Oh, yes, you are, Laura,' he drawled softly, her limbs trembling at the hard, flat note of certainty in his voice.

Two days later as she sat on the beach, staring glumly out over the ocean, Laura knew that she couldn't fool herself any longer. Ross had, in fact, been quite right— and what she was going to do about the problem, she simply had no idea.

Turning her head, she gazed over to where her husband and the two little girls, together with their friend, Kerry-Jane, were busily engaged in filling their buckets with damp sand. Directing the building of what appeared to be a large fortification, Ross was clearly enjoying himself as he laughed and joked with the children, as perfectly at ease in these casual, unsophisticated surroundings as he was in the cosmopolitan offices of a smart City boardroom.

With a heavy sigh she lay back on the pile of beach cushions, closing her eyes against the early-morning sun, already climbing high in the sky.

The discovery that she was—*goodness knows why*—still in love with her husband was something she had fought hard and long against over the past few days. And she might have been able to deal with the situation—might, indeed, have been able to suppress and finally bury such an errant emotion—if it weren't for her present situation. How *could* she possibly do her best to forget Ross when she was now forced, for the very best of reasons, to live cheek by jowl with him for twenty-four hours a day? And she might even have managed to survive *that* sort of difficult scenario if it hadn't been for the alarming, almost intimidating atmosphere engendered by Ross.

Ever since that morning when he'd briefly pinned her to the mattress, gazing down at her so intently that his eyes had seemed to search her very soul, she'd realised that she was in deep trouble. He *knew* that, despite all her denials, she was still violently attracted to him. And, if she'd had any illusions about being able to deceive him, his behaviour over the past two days had put paid to that.

Everywhere she turned, whatever she was doing, Laura was almost tangibly aware of his hard grey eyes focused on her increasingly nervous figure. It was as if he was just biding his time. As if he knew that he only had to put his arms around her for her to immediately surrender, to succumb, a willing victim, to the force of his dark enchantment.

Frightened as much by her own emotional weakness as by the almost dangerous, threatening atmosphere which seemed to be building up between them, she was beginning to feel like some poor rabbit caught in a trap. And there was *nothing* she could do about it! She couldn't even accuse him of laying a finger on her, since she was always fast asleep when he joined her in the large bed, and the twins arrived to wake her up in the morning. It was only the lingering aroma of his cologne and the rumpled sheets that betrayed the fact that he spent his nights lying beside her.

She was feeling almost physically sick with nerves, and increasingly plagued by tension headaches. For him to know that she was still very much sexually attracted to him was bad enough—but she was terrified of Ross discovering that her feelings ran much deeper. That, despite the past five years, she had never stopped loving him.

What on earth was she going to do?

CHAPTER SEVEN

'Now, do you think that's enough, honey, or shall I see what else we've got in the ice-box?'

'Enough. . .?' Laura gave a weak laugh. 'Forget the picnic—there must be enough food here to feed an army!'

'I can see you don't know much about kids.' Carole Meadows gave her a wry smile as she began filling the picnic hamper. 'The twins and Kerry-Jane might not have much flesh on them, but boy—they sure can pack it away!' she laughed. 'In fact, you'll soon find out that three square meals a day is hardly scratching the surface—most kids seem to have an ever-open stomach.'

Laura gave her a wry smile. 'Yes, I can see that I have a lot to learn.' She hesitated for a moment, before adding with a worried frown, 'I wish I wasn't feeling so nervous about having to cope with the twins back at the apartment in New York.'

'Hey—relax! You'll be fine,' the other woman quickly reassured her. 'I've watched you with the kids, and, while I know it can't be easy, you seem to be doing a grand job. It's plain to see that you love those little girls.'

Laura nodded. 'Yes, I do,' she replied simply. 'They're so sweet and amusing, but. . .well, they're also pretty exhausting, too,' she admitted with a small sigh.

It seemed absolutely pathetic that, at her relatively

young age, she should be feeling so tired and weary at the end of each day. Last night, for instance, she'd been barely able to keep her eyes open during dinner.

When she said as much to Carole the other woman gave a hoot of wry laughter.

'So, what makes you think you're any different from the rest of us?' she grinned. 'Honest to God, I don't reckon I had one good night's sleep until Kerry-Jane was well over two years old. I can tell you—I was almost propping my eyelids up with matchsticks by the time Ben used to get back from the office! So don't you worry, OK?' she added, giving Laura a warm, reassuring smile. 'Besides, you've got Ross to help out, haven't you?'

'Er—yes, I suppose I have.'

Carole didn't appear to notice the English girl's slightly hesitant reply as she continued enthusiastically, 'He's proving to be a terrific father-figure, isn't he? And it's obvious that he is just crazy about *you*, honey. Why, he can hardly keep his eyes off you!' She smiled at the sudden flush staining the other girl's pale cheeks.

I wish he *would* keep his eyes off me, Laura thought grimly, feeling certain that she must have experienced almost a lifetime's amount of tension over the past few days. In fact, it wasn't just the twins who were solely responsible for her feeling so exhausted. The nervous stress and strain of being forced to be in Ross's company, each and every day, had really taken a heavy toll on her reserves of strength. And the tension seemed to have affected her in other ways, too. She'd never had a weight problem, of course, but she must have lost a few pounds over the past few days, because the waistband of the shorts she was wearing this morning—which she had purchased in New York only last Saturday—was already far looser than it had been.

'Good idea; the traffic on the expressway was going to be really awful this morning.'

'Hmm. . .?' Laura blinked, realising that she had been so buried in her own thoughts that she'd missed what Carole had been saying.

'I was just telling you that I reckon it was a good idea—to wait a day before going back to New York,' Carole repeated, smiling to herself at the other girl's slightly abstracted expression.

Laura and Ross were such an outstandingly good-looking couple, and obviously so very much in love. Of course, she hadn't been joking when she'd told the English girl that a marriage between two highly charged Leos could be an explosive situation. One of her friends had married a man with the same late-July birthday as his wife—and what a knock-out, drag-out marriage that had been! Unhappily, it had only lasted a few short weeks, but all their friends still shuddered at the memory of their truly spectacular fights!

However, Ross and Laura were obviously quite different. As she'd said to Ben when they'd been getting ready to go to bed last night, you could practically *feel* the highly charged sexy atmosphere between that pair of love-birds! Maybe it might be a good idea for her and Ben to have a holiday in England? She was awfully fond of her husband, of course, but there was no denying that their own lovemaking had become just a little predictable. She'd have to lose some weight, of course, and then maybe buy some new sexy underwear. . . But if a trip abroad could result in Ben giving her some of those hot, steamy looks that handsome Ross was throwing his own wife's way—well, she wouldn't complain too much about that!

'Are you sure you don't mind having us stay on for another day?' Laura asked anxiously. 'You've both been *so* kind and helpful—I don't know what we'd have done without you and Ben.'

'It's been our pleasure,' Carole assured her earnestly. 'And it has to be a good idea to stay on here, in the Hamptons, until tomorrow,' she added as she finished packing up the hampers. 'Not only will everyone be rushing back to the city today, after the weekend vacation, but I understand Ross has been on the phone, getting the air-conditioning fixed and also seeing about someone to help you with the kids. They must really be looking forward to seeing their parents again.'

Laura nodded. 'Yes, it's been *such* a relief to hear that Liz and Owen are still making good progress. Although. . .well, it does look as though it's going to be a long time before they can leave hospital,' she added sorrowfully.

'I know, honey. It's a really terrible thing to have happened to such a sweet couple,' Carole murmured warmly, putting a comforting arm about the other girl's shoulder. 'Does that mean you're going to be in New York for some time?'

'I—er—I really don't know.' Laura gave a small, helpless shrug of her shoulders. She'd been so preoccupied with first the tragedy, and then her concern for the twins' welfare, that she hadn't given any thought to the future.

'I'm sure everything will work out—so don't you

worry,' Carole was saying as Ross, accompanied by the twins, came into the kitchen. 'Your picnic is ready,' she told him with a beaming smile. 'So, off you all go—and mind you have a good time!'

And, to Laura's surprise, they did. Although the twins were disappointed that Kerry-Jane was away for the day, on a visit to her grandmother, they happily helped with packing the picnic into the car. And, with the two little girls squeezed into the narrow rear seat of that sports car, Ross had driven along the coast before discovering a quietly sheltered and deserted bay.

While Laura unpacked the picnic, before joining Emma and Sophie to search for shells along the shore, Ross managed to find enough driftwood to build a small fire. They didn't really need it, of course, since it was a lovely warm summer's day, but the twins clearly thought it a great adventure, busily insisting on helping Ross by scampering about the bay in search of small pieces of wood to add to the bonfire. And when Ross, impaling some pieces of chicken on the end of long sticks, promised to show them how to barbecue the joints they were thrilled, after the meat was cooked, to sink their teeth into the hot, if slightly charred, meat.

As they made their way slowly home in the late afternoon, Laura sighed with contentment as she viewed the peaceful farm fields between the towns and villages, which stretched hazily into the distance and embodied the stillness of an old and continuing way of life. Against all the odds, it had proved to be a happy and companionable day, Ross's unusually calm, friendly manner towards her having released much of the stresses and

strains that had previously left her feeling so tense and
nervous.

It really seemed as if Ross had been determined to
make sure the day was a success. Clearly in a relaxed
frame of mind, he'd been kind, considerate and amusing,
making no reference to his personal involvement with
her. He had, in fact, treated her as a man might well
treat a wife to whom he'd been married for some years—
a relaxed, comfortable relationship in which there was
no need for any outward signs of affection. And, indeed,
the need to look after the twins, keeping them busily
entertained and happy during the day, had obviously
helped to keep both their minds off their troubled
personal relationship.

She was still desperately aware of him, of course.
There seemed nothing she could do about the deeply
dismaying, sick feelings of nervous excitement whenever
she was anywhere near his tall, rangy figure. It was
almost as if she was suffering from some dreadful disease
that could only be cured by his physical removal. And,
if so, she could only fervently hope and pray that Liz
and Owen's recovery was as speedy as possible.

There had been only one moment to cause her any
undue alarm. Laughingly agreeing to help one of the
little girls, who had been determined to dig a deep
hole—'all the way down to Australia'—she'd peeled off
her jade-green T-shirt and matching shorts, to reveal
her brief bikini. And almost immediately she'd felt the
forceful beam of Ross's hard grey eyes sweeping over her
slender figure.

Purchased during that mad shopping trip at
Bloomingdales, the minuscule garment in watery shades

of blue and green had been by far the most decent item among the swimwear items bought for her by Ross. Which wasn't saying much, she'd thought gloomily, glancing down at the brief scraps of material. Laura wasn't ashamed of her slender waist and full bosom, but neither was she used to displaying her figure in such a blatant manner.

But, with the gleam from beneath her husband's heavy, sleepy eyelids practically scorching her flesh, Laura had quickly struggled back into her T-shirt.

'There's no need to cover yourself up—certainly not for my benefit,' he'd drawled in a tone that had sent shivers quivering frantically up and down her spine. And she'd been glumly aware that her quick retort, 'I'm not—I just felt a bit cold for a moment,' had sounded remarkably unconvincing.

However, save for that brief and embarrassing episode, the day had continued to be one of great enjoyment. Laura had felt, for perhaps the first time since her husband's reappearance in her life, the warmth of a shared companionship.

Arriving back at the large beach house, she took the two sleepy children upstairs to their large bedroom, firmly overriding their protests that no, they really didn't want a bath by pointing out to them that they were still covered with sand and sea water. And because she, too, was feeling hot and sticky she decided to join the girls in the nursery suite's jacuzzi—one of three such glamorous items in the large house.

Having taken a change of clothes and underwear to the beach with her, she was able to put on a fresh dress before tucking the children into bed.

When she finally came downstairs it was to find Carole insisting that, since this was their last night in the Hamptons before returning to the apartment in New York, she'd arranged for them to have a romantic candle-lit dinner in their cottage.

'I'll baby-sit the kids,' Carole insisted over Laura's blushing and increasingly desperate protests that there was no need to go to such trouble. 'It's no trouble, honey,' her hostess was assuring her as they were joined by Ben and Ross. 'You'd like some time on your own with Laura, wouldn't you?' Carole smilingly asked the tall Englishman.

Ross's smooth reply, 'Yes, indeed. That's very kind of you,' was the signal to set a tide of deep apprehension coursing through Laura's veins. Surely neither of the Meadowses could possibly have missed the deep sardonic note in his voice?

Trying to control the trembling in her legs, which felt as though they were made of cotton wool, Laura silently followed Ross across the green lawns to their guest cottage, where Carole had laid out the cold supper. Laura could have almost wept as she viewed the cold salmon and potato salad, the strawberries and cream, and the bottle of champagne nestling in its bed of ice. For how could Carole—a truly kind, sweet and very generous person—have guessed that a romantic dinner for two was the very last thing on their minds?

Desperately trying to think of something to say, she heard behind her the sound of Ross clearing his throat.

'I don't know about you, but I'm really not feeling very hungry at the moment. In fact, since it's such a hot night—why don't we go and cool off with a swim?'

Turning around to peer up at him in the gathering darkness, Laura had no clue what he was thinking as she viewed his bland expression, which echoed the studied unconcern in his voice. And, since she, too, wasn't at all hungry—and would have done practically *anything* to avoid having to sit down at such an overtly romantic candle-lit dinner—she reluctantly agreed to his suggestion.

'Come on, then,' he said, reaching forward to take her hand.

'No, I... I've just got to put on a swimsuit,' she muttered, taking a nervous step backwards.

'Of course, if you want to,' he agreed smoothly, the relaxed tone in his voice helping to calm her nameless fears. 'I'll go ahead, and you can join me down on the beach.'

Struggling into yet another of the brief garments bought for her by Ross—her trembling fingers fumbling awkwardly with the small scraps of material—Laura dearly wished that she had the courage to chicken out of the whole affair. But she knew that, if she didn't turn up on the beach, Ross would only come back to fetch her.

With a heavy sigh, and not even daring to look at her slim, almost naked form in the mirror, Laura slowly made her way out of the cottage, and down towards the ocean. Although the moon was riding high in the sky, and shedding a rather weird, eerie glow on the flowering shrubs and various trees edging the green lawn, she was surprised at how much more calm and at ease she felt in the soft, enveloping darkness as she picked her way carefully over the sand.

Standing by the water's edge, Laura glanced ner-

vously about her, but there appeared to be no sign of
Ross. Walking slowly into the ocean, which was as still
as a mill-pond, she couldn't help relishing the feel of the
cool salty water on her heated flesh. Still able to feel the
firm sand beneath her feet, she swam quietly for a few
minutes, before turning over on to her back. Gently
rocked by the smooth, rhythmic action of the calm sea,
she gazed up at the sky above. It was an extraordinary
sensation, floating here in the inky darkness, with moon-
beams dancing off the top of the small waves, and the
twinkling stars above shining through the moth-eaten
blanket of the night sky. It was as if she was all alone—
a tiny speck on the ocean, surrounded by a galaxy that
seemed to stretch out into infinity.

Despite being caught up in an almost mystical trance,
Laura had not entirely forgotten that she wasn't the only
person swimming in the ocean. And yet, as she floated
in a dream-like state, she felt no alarm when she slowly
became aware that she was not alone, almost tele-
pathically sensing his presence, even before the dark,
sleek head of Ross quietly surfaced in the water beside
her, barely disturbing the total peace and silence of their
surroundings.

Although she did not even turn to look at him, a
delicious warmth began to spread through her inert
form—as though some electrical force was quietly pulsing across the few feet of water separating their bodies.
Her whole being seemed to be pervaded by a dreamy
languor, a torpid drowsiness, which was barely disturbed
as his hand closed over her wrist. And then, so gently
that she was hardly aware of what was happening—as if
she was merely swaying with the tide—he gradually

pulled her towards the shore, slowly drawing her up against the bare, damp skin of his broad chest.

'You're like some beautiful sea nymph. . .' he whispered softly in her ear, his hands protectively holding her slim body as, half standing and half floating in the water, she wound her arms about his neck.

Dreamily, the blood flowing slowly through her veins like a stream of thick honey, she gradually felt her breasts swell and harden against the rough hairs of his chest. As she drifted mindlessly in the shimmering water all her resistance to the past few days seemed to be dissolving away within the strength and power of his embrace. She sighed as she felt his mouth gently touching hers, before the sweet warmth of his tongue parted her lips to avidly savour the inner softness of her mouth.

The touch of his cool hands, now moving enticingly over her body in a voluptuous, slow caress, began to break through her trance-like state. She shuddered as she felt him unfastening the catch of her bikini-top, her heart starting to pound with a heavy beat as the pressure of his kiss became fiercer and more demanding. And then, as he pulled her hungrily closer to him, she became forcefully aware that he was naked, the hard thrust of his flesh causing shock waves of erotic excitement to zigzag through her quivering figure.

For a brief moment she tried to summon up some form of resistance, as if by an effort of will she could deny her immediate instinctive reaction to his dark enchantment. But the effort to combat her own sensual response seemed too much to cope with—slipping away far beyond her reach. With a small, helpless moan she surrendered to the muscular arms tightening like a vice about her, gazing up at his hawk-like features thrown into sharp, dramatic relief by the pale moonlight, and trembling at the dangerous gleam in the eyes devouring her from beneath their heavy lids.

And then, as if the slight sound which had broken from her throat was a signal, he quickly scooped her up in his arms, wading swiftly through the shallow water towards the sandy shore.

'No. . .' she whispered tremulously as he marched across the sand towards the dark lawns leading up to the cottage. 'This is madness. . .!'

'Oh, no!' he gave a deep rumble of laughter, the sound echoing menacingly in her ear, which was pressed so closely to his broad chest. 'We've had five years of madness—it's about time we had some sanity in our lives!'

Her limbs trembled, her heart beginning to pound like a sledge-hammer at the note of hard determination in his voice, which betrayed no weakness or breathlessness, evidence—if she'd needed it—of his superbly fit physique.

'Oh, no, Ross—this is a terrible mistake!' she cried in a desperate attempt to cling on to some form of sanity, wriggling violently to try and escape his embrace as he almost ran up the steps and entered the cottage.

Taking no notice of her breathless protest, he barely halted his stride as he kicked open the bedroom door. She only had a bare glimpse of the softly lit room, her struggling figure still clasped firmly in his arms, as he continued through to the *en suite* bathroom. Setting her firmly down on the wide base of the large shower cubicle, he swiftly turned on the taps, before joining her beneath the cascade of fresh water. Emotionally dazed and confused, she leaned weakly against his hard, muscular body, only the support of his strong tanned arms preventing her trembling legs from giving way beneath her as he swiftly removed the lower half of her bikini.

Despite his firm statement on the beach, Laura knew that this was all a dreadful mistake. With one part of her bemused and disorientated mind she *knew* that she must call a halt—right now! But knowing what she ought to do was one thing—putting it into action seemed to be quite another. As his strong hands began to gently sponge the sand and sea water from her trembling body her emotions seemed to be spinning out of control. And, just as the fine-needle spray of water flowed down over her shaking figure, so all sense and caution drained away from her dazed mind.

His fingers laced themselves in the loose strands of her wet hair, pulling her head back so that her body was arched against him, forcing her to face the feverish gleam in the heavy-lidded grey eyes staring down at her so intently.

And then she was lost. The rampant desire she glimpsed in his eyes was so clear and so fierce that she felt her breath catch in her throat. A deep responsive pulse seemed to begin pounding deep in her stomach, and she knew that she wanted him every bit as much as he wanted her, that every fibre of her being was throbbing with the compulsive drive of passionate need and desire. His soapy hands slipped possessively over her quivering body, pausing to sensually caress the hard, swollen peaks of her breasts before trailing a slow, scorching path down over her slim waist, and on down. . .down over the soft swell of her hips. And then his iron control seemed to give way for a moment, his fingers clenching as he pulled her roughly against him.

With a breathless gasp at the clear reminder of his hard arousal, she trembled helplessly, swept away by the force and potency of her own desire. She wanted to run her hands over the firm masculine planes of his body, the broad shoulders and narrow hips, his long, muscular thighs. Trembling helplessly, she pressed her hands against his chest, her fingertips of their own volition moving through the short, rough curly hair to brush the hard, flat nipples of his chest.

'*Laura*. . .!' he groaned, a deep, compulsive inner hunger shaking his tall figure as her hands trailed gently downwards, following the dark arrow of hair over the taut muscles of his stomach, which clenched violently at her soft touch. A hoarse, muffled groan broke from his throat, his powerful body shuddering as her fingers came to rest on the hard, swollen thrust of his pulsing flesh. Her small, incoherent moan caused him to clasp her tightly against his body for a moment, before lifting her damp figure up in his arms and carrying her back through into the bedroom.

'Oh, Ross. . .' she sighed helplessly as he lowered her damp body on to the cool sheets. 'We can't. . .we must. . .we must talk. . .'

'For God's sake, Laura—this is not the time for conversation!' He gave a low, husky laugh as he lay down beside her, bending his head to her throat and pressing his lips to the pulse that was beating so wildly under her skin. 'We'll talk later—much later. . .' he murmured softly, slipping an arm beneath her trembling body so that her breasts were lifted towards him, his lips trailing a scorching path over her quivering flesh, a deep ache gripping her loins as his mouth sought and found the hard swollen peaks of her breasts.

Barely able to control her shivering delight and excitement as his lips and tongue rhythmically stroked her swollen nipples, while his hands sensuously caressed her body, she shuddered violently as she felt the warmth of his skin against her own soft flesh, the gentle pressure of his fingers as he stroked her thighs.

It was five long years since any man—*this man*—had intimately touched her like this; five years in which she'd held at bay these deep torrents of emotion, which would not now be denied. She was almost fainting at the aching torment of mounting pleasure aroused by the erotic caress of his mouth and hands. Her helpless moans of delight seemed to excite his own desire, perspiration breaking out on his skin as his body began moving against her with a rhythmic urgency he could barely control. And then, in an agony of desperate need and passion, she was reaching for him as his body came down upon hers.

'Ross. . .please, Ross. . .!' she gasped, desperate for the power and thrust of his flesh, which alone could bring release from the ever-mounting, passionate excitement that was shaking her slender form. She clung to him while he held himself hard and poised over her for a moment, and then he parted her qivering thighs, slipping himself high inside her as naturally as a silver shoehorn easing on a silk slipper. As he moved slowly at first his mouth sought first her breasts and then her lips, his breathing ragged as the pulsating, rhythmic movement quickened, echoing the rising heat in her blood, both of them caught up in a swirling vortex of emotions. And she cried out as a cascade of fireworks seemed to explode deep within her, before their bodies, now moving in perfect unison, recaptured the fierce, tumultuous pleasure they had always shared in the past—the total consummation which she had been denied for so long.

Cradled within his arms, Laura drifted into a deep sleep, but, even as she dreamed, their bodies seemed to stir against one another, as if they couldn't help but touch and make love again; as if nothing could satisfy the desire that each had awakened in the other's flesh. And then, as the pale light of morning crept in through the window, she was awoken by the feel of his mouth on her breasts. Their limbs entwined, he slowly and gently at first and then with a mounting fierceness made love to her again, his eyes gleaming with the triumph of possession as her pliant body instantly surrendered, both to his sensual touch and the low, husky murmur of his voice. She felt the heat of his skin against hers, the rising tide of hot passion overwhelming them once again, and there was no more time for gentle, slow lovemaking. He entered her fiercely, her body and all her senses filled with him until, as before, the slumbering embers of the fire he had lit last night now blazed again, the raging flames consuming them both.

Her heart still pounding, Laura moved restlessly within his arms. 'Ross. . .?'

'Mmm?' he murmured sleepily, drawing her body closer to his lithe figure.

'Ross—we have to talk,' she muttered. 'You know that the twins always seem to get up at the crack of dawn. And there's so much. . .so much we haven't discussed, or. . .'

His low chuckle and the touch of his finger tips drifting lightly over her curves were making it difficult for her to concentrate.

'I promise you that we will have a long talk—and sort out everything between us, once and for all,' he murmured, burying his face in her blonde hair for a moment, before raising himself up on an elbow to gaze down at her lovely face.

'However. . .' he continued softly, the breath catching in her throat as his fingers began moving slowly and erotically over her body.

'You can't!' she gasped helplessly, unable to prevent a trembling response to his intimate touch. 'Not *again*!'

He gave a low rumble of husky laughter. 'Oh, no?' he drawled mockingly as he slowly lowered his dark head towards her. 'I wouldn't take a bet on it, if I were you!'

CHAPTER EIGHT

BRUSHING the damp hair from her brow, Laura stared drearily at herself in the mirror.

So much for the glamorous, stylish Leo woman! she thought glumly, remembering Carole Meadows' words. In fact, she could only be profoundly grateful that none of her business colleagues or any of her smart friends back in London was able to see her looking *so* awful.

Glancing despairingly down at what—only a few hours ago—had been a crisp, smart cotton dress in her favourite shade of sapphire-blue, but which was now crumpled and covered with sticky finger-marks, she gave a heavy sigh. Vanity was a sin, of course, and she knew that her appearance was completely irrelevant when compared to the importance of caring for Liz's two little girls. But why had nobody ever told her that it was quite *impossible* to keep clean whenever there were any children about? She dearly loved the twins, but over the last two days, since they'd returned to Liz and Owen's apartment, her cousin's ancient washing-machine had seemed to be going non-stop!

The scorching, clammy heat of a summer in New York had been a total physical shock. Completely unaccustomed to the hot, humid air—so wet and steamy that it was almost impossible to breathe properly—she'd been deeply grateful for the air-conditioning in the apartment which—*when* it was working properly!—had kept them all relatively cool. But within five minutes of her putting a foot on the pavement outside the large building she'd found that she might as well be in a hot and steamy sauna bath.

However, leaving aside the intolerable heat, there was no doubt that New York was a really amazing place. Even in this mainly residential area, the pace of life appeared to be at least two or three times that of London—which now seemed practically moribund in comparison to the tempo and sheer adrenalin of this exciting city. Not that she'd had much time to explore it, of course. But yesterday morning, when she and the twins had accompanied Ross downtown to a brief business meeting on Wall Street, she'd been deeply impressed by the dramatic skyscrapers rising like icons to the modern age—representing the excitement and violence of change and, above all, the massive power of money. It appeared to be a city which could cater to anything one's heart desired: all varieties of food from the six continents, restaurants and bars open twenty-four hours a day, and everything else under the sun easily available just for the cost of a phone call.

Nothing could have been a greater contrast to the Hamptons—where miles and miles of unspoilt coastline and white sands edged the rugged Atlantic Ocean. The peace and serenity of the green countryside and sandy dunes seemed almost a lifetime away from her present existence—as did the night she had spent in Ross's arms.

Woken the next morning, yet again, by the early arrival of the twins, there had simply been no opportunity to do more than groggily force herself to rise, dressing herself and the children before completing the packing of all their suitcases.

Even after bidding a fond farewell to Ben and Carole Meadows, there still hadn't been the opportunity to have anything other than a few brief casual words with Ross as he'd driven them all back to New York. And any hope Laura might have had of at last having that 'long talk' which Ross had so faithfully promised her had been dashed on opening the front door of the apartment.

It was one thing to lose your husband to another woman—but how could she possibly compete with the manifold attractions of a fax machine?

'There the beastly thing goes *again*!' she grumbled under her breath, grimacing at herself in the mirror as she caught the faint hum and slight clattering sound from the living-room, where the machine was clearly spewing forth yet more reams of urgent letters and company reports from all over the world. And unfortunately, since she could actually hear the machine from the bedroom, it meant that the air-conditioning was on the blink once more!

With a heavy sigh Laura placed her elbows on the dressing-table, leaning forward to bury her face in her hands for a moment. It wasn't just the fact that she was going to have to make her umpteenth phone call, asking the electrical repair man to call at the apartment yet again, which was so deeply depressing; her own personal life—like that of the antiquated air-conditioning system—seemed to keep breaking down just when she was hopeful of a permanent repair. Surely, after the wonderful night of passion she had experienced with Ross, they'd had a *real* chance of mending their relationship? And yet, ever since they had returned to New York, Laura had barely had more than a few minutes' private conversation with her husband.

When they'd first re-entered the apartment the place had been crawling with a crowd of men who were mending the air-conditioning, installing a computer and modem to a fresh telephone line, and plugging in the dreaded fax machine.

'I see that you've been busy!' she'd muttered sourly to Ross.

'Yes, I have, haven't I,' he had agreed cheerfully, clearly pleased at the speedy, efficient response to the phone calls he'd made from the Meadowses' ranch house the day before.

And that had just about been *that*! Laura told herself glumly. The twins had been thrilled with the computer, of course—how was it that even small children could pick up the mechanics of these complicated machines in five seconds flat? And in the mid-afternoon, only a few hours after they had arrived back at the apartment, an urgent message had come through for Ross by fax. The expression on his face had grown hard and grim as he'd scanned the paper in his hands, before angrily crunching it up into a ball and hurling it into a nearby waste-paper basket.

'What's wrong?' she'd asked as he'd begun pacing up and down the room.

'A large multi-national conglomerate are trying to take over my business,' he told her tersely. 'I don't know if they've got wind of Owen's accident—but, unfortunately, their timing is perfect!'

'What are you going to do?' She gazed at him with a worried frown. 'What *can* you do?'

He gave a harsh bark of angry laughter. 'I'm going to fight them, of course—to the last ditch, if necessary. I'll make those bastards wish they'd never been born!' he added savagely, before grabbing the telephone and calling his office in London.

And from that moment to this there had been no opportunity for any kind of personal discussion. Working flat out during the day, and immersed in reams of paperwork during the night, Ross had been totally absorbed in his battle to fight off the sharks who were attacking his financial empire.

Yet how could she possibly complain? It was those very firebrand qualities of ruthless daring, initiative and enterprise which had drawn her to him in the first place. His single-minded pursuit of his objectives—which had originally led him to sweep her off her feet in such a masterly fashion— and his instinctive opposition to the challenge before him now were qualities which Laura found truly admirable. And since, unlike many wives of city moguls, she'd had recent experience at the sharp end of business in the City of London, she understood, only too clearly, the problems he was facing at the present time.

All of which, unfortunately, meant that she had no alternative but to put her own personal feelings to one side. And although Ross had insisted on regularly visiting his brother and sister-in-law in hospital, it was on Laura's own slim shoulders that most of the daily problems had fallen. Keeping the twins happy and contented was, in itself, a full-time job. But, since the small apartment was in danger of becoming snowed under, principally by Ross's files and paperwork, she'd tentatively suggested that they might move into larger and more modern surroundings. A suggestion which Ross had instantly rejected.

'This is the only home that the children have ever known,' he had told her irritably when she'd tentatively raised the question. 'I know it isn't very convenient. . .'

'That must be the understatement of the year!'

'. . .but, with their parents in hospital, I feel any such move would be counter-productive,' he'd added curtly, dismissing the subject as he'd turned back to the pile of papers in front of him.

Staring down at the dark head bent over his work, Laura had found herself swept by diametrically opposed emotions. Despite being filled with an overwhelming love and compassion for her husband, who was single-handedly fighting off one of the world's largest corporations, she'd also been swept by a strong desire to bash him over the head with his own fax machine! How *could* he have made mad, passionate love to her one moment—and been able to ignore both her and their marriage problems the next? Surely he couldn't be so insensitive? Surely he must be aware of her deep unhappiness and frustration at the vague, unsettled state of their relationship?

You must be joking! she told herself grimly, recalled to the present by the sound of the fax machine, once again clattering away in the other room. The damned man had always been a total workaholic. And, as far as she could see, he hadn't changed one iota!

The fact that she was worried about her *own* career

seemed to be a matter of little interest as far as Ross was concerned. She'd been in touch with Tim Dunton, of course. Although he'd assured her that there were no problems, and that she mustn't worry her pretty head about her clients, who were sure to understand her problems, Laura still couldn't help feeling slightly anxious. As she had said to Julie when she'd phoned her yesterday, even when returning to the office from a short holiday, in the fast-moving world of the City of London you could never be *entirely* sure that your desk would still be there!

Julie had been very sympathetic, which had helped to soothe the anxiety about her job. Thanks to her profession as a teacher, Julie had also been able to suggest several ideas to help Laura entertain and amuse the twins.

Greatly to her relief, the first visit of the little girls to the hospital to see their parents hadn't been nearly as traumatic as Laura had feared. Liz and Owen were clearly making good progress, and, apart from a few tearful moments, the twins had happily settled down, regarding their trips to the hospital as part of their daily routine.

Putting out a hand to pick up her brush, intending to try to do something about her limp blonde hair, Laura gave a yelp of dismay as she caught sight of the time on her wrist-watch. She'd only got five minutes in which to change out of this crumpled dress and fix her make-up before interviewing yet another applicant for the job of a daily nanny to help her look after the twins. Luckily Emma and Sophie were spending part of the afternoon with one of their friends, who lived in an apartment two floors down. So she'd be able to have a few moments of peace and quiet in which to interview the woman.

Quickly slipping into a sleeveless straight shirt-waister dress of pink shantung, Laura was just fastening the last button when she heard the sound of the doorbell. At least this one is punctual, she told herself, quickly checking her appearance in a full-length mirror before, mentally crossing her fingers for luck, she hurried through the living-room to answer the door.

'You look good enough to eat!' Ross said some hours later as he entered the apartment while she was giving the children their supper. 'How did you get on today—have you found a nanny to help you with the children?' he added, throwing her into confusion by casually giving her a peck on the cheek before leaning across the table and helping himself to a slice of chocolate cake.

'Yes—keep your fingers crossed—I think I've actually found someone at last,' she told him with a thankful sigh.

Despite having been in touch with many agencies, they'd only had five applicants so far—four of whom had been absolutely hopeless. One woman had spoken only French, another only Spanish. The third had said she couldn't possibly 'touch a job where the mother was at home', while the fourth had merely gazed supercili-ously around the apartment, before announcing that it was 'not up to my standards'. And when, after the girl had gone, Laura had gazed about the chaotic-looking living-room, she'd had to agree that it wasn't up to her standards, either.

'Quite frankly, I can't believe my luck—she appeared

to be an absolute paragon!' Laura told Ross now as he poured himself a cool drink. 'She said the salary was quite acceptable, and she even pronounced herself charmed by this apartment—how about that?'

'Humph,' Ross grunted doubtfully. 'What's this paragon's name?'

'Angelique. She was apparently christened Ann, but, as she informed me, "I think Angelique is more *me*, somehow," ' Laura grinned.

'Very New York!' Ross grinned back at her as he leaned forward, helping himself to another slice of chocolate cake. 'I must say, this is *absolutely* delicious—did you make it?'

'Yes, yes, I did,' she told him, feeling ridiculously pleased that he was clearly enjoying her first attempt at baking a cake. She'd never thought she was cut out for the domestic life, but she was surprised to find just how satisfying and fulfilling it really was.

'So, when's this—er—Angelique starting work?' Ross asked.

'She's promised to come first thing tomorrow. The girl really did seem perfect, and she also has some very good references,' Laura assured him.

'What did you think, girls?' he asked the twins.

'We thought she was really stupid!' one of the twins announced, before they both collapsed into a fit of giggles.

'That's not at all a nice thing to say, Emma,' Laura told her sternly. Since she had decided to give Emma a pink headband and Sophie a blue one it was a relief to know, at last, which twin she was talking to.

The little girl giggled again. 'I'm not Emma—I'm Sophie!'

'But you're wearing pink, and——'

'Oh, we thought that was a silly idea,' the other twin retorted, before both the children and, regrettably, Ross as well burst into peals of laughter.

Taking a deep breath, and casting her eyes up to the ceiling while she slowly counted to ten, Laura decided that motherhood was a highly overrated occupation.

'That's enough nonsense, you two,' Ross told the twins with mock-seriousness. 'It's time for bed. So, off you go, and I'll be through to read you a story in a few minutes.'

Watching as the twins scampered from the room, Laura was surprised to find Ross's arm sliding about her waist. 'You look tired,' he said, raising a hand to brush a lock of hair away from her brow.

'Yes. . .yes, it's been a long day,' she admitted, her cheeks flushing and her heart beginning to beat in a crazy rhythm as he held her tightly against his hard, tall figure for a moment. The musky male scent of his cologne teased her nostrils, and she was ashamed at the way her knees were trembling as he led her over to sit down on the wide, comfortable couch.

'I'm glad to hear that you've found someone to help you with the children at last,' he said, sitting down on the sofa beside her. 'Particularly since it seems I have no alternative but to fly back to London this evening.'

'*What*. . .?' she gasped. 'You can't possibly. . .you *can't* leave me here, in New York, alone with the children!' she exclaimed helplessly, panicking at the thought of being solely responsible for the two little girls.

'Calm down, Laura,' he told her firmly. 'I'm only going to be away for forty-eight hours. . .'

She gave a high-pitched incredulous laugh. 'What do you mean by "only"? That sounds almost a lifetime to me at the moment!' she wailed, waving her hands distractedly in the air.

'Oh, come on—it's not that bad!' He frowned impatiently down at her. 'You've just hired someone to help you with the children, and I've already laid on a cleaning lady.'

'Correction! She refers to herself as a "household technician",' Laura snorted grimly. 'The woman was disgusted to find that we did *not* have a microwave oven for her to polish, and she has a doctor's certificate to say she cannot bend down. In fact, I seem to have spent most of this morning cooking the lunch she ordered!'

'Really, Laura!' He shrugged dismissively. 'I know nothing about the domestic side of life—and I don't intend to start getting involved with it now.'

'I don't know anything about it, either—and *I* wouldn't have anything to do with it if there were any alternative,' she retorted bitterly.

'I really don't see the problem. . .'

'You wouldn't!'

'. . .and, in any case, cooking and looking after children is strictly women's work,' he told her flatly. 'Now, I must go and read the children that story I promised them, and then I'll have to pack my case,' he added, clearly considering the subject closed as he patted her hand before rising from the couch and walking away towards the twins' bedroom.

Her sapphire-blue eyes glinting with anger, Laura glared after his tall figure.

Men! That old cliché 'a woman's place is in the home' was a perfect cop-out! She was a career woman—and the fact that she'd found herself actually enjoying looking after the children, and doing the cooking, was neither here nor there!

Ross had no right to automatically expect her to suddenly become an efficient home-maker, she grumbled to herself as she got up to clear the dirty plates from the small dining-room table. And it wasn't until she'd finished doing the washing-up, and the kitchen had been cleaned to her satisfaction, that she began at last to simmer down.

Her first responsibility was to the children, she acknowledged with a sigh. She couldn't take their mother's place, of course, but for Liz's sake she must try to do everything she possibly could for the little girls. The fact that she was used to living in an expensive, glamorous apartment in London, and held down an equally glamorous if exhausting job, had little or no relevance at the moment. While Ross was fighting to save his business—rather like David against Goliath— he really couldn't be expected to deal with the boringly mundane but nevertheless important work of running the apartment as efficiently as possible. And it hadn't been fair of her to expect him to do so.

Having given herself a good talking to, and feeling ashamed of her misplaced, foolish pride, Laura made her way into the twins' small bedroom, where Ross had just finished telling them a story. Tucking the little girls up under their light sheets, she couldn't prevent tears from coming to her eyes when one of the children placed her thin arms around her neck.

'We're sorry that we teased you—and I promise to wear my blue headband tomorrow,' Sophie whispered in her ear.

And then, as she sat on one of the small bunks and listened as the twins said their prayers, the last remnants of her bruised pride vanished when Ross gave her shoulder a warm, affectionate squeeze.

But, as she trailed after him into their own bedroom, leaning against the door while he quickly packed his case, she realised that she'd already lost him. Even as he lifted from a cupboard the freshly ironed shirts, about which he was so particular, he was already mentally back in England. And his next words confirmed it.

'The Friday night flights are always crowded,' he told her with a shrug. 'But I'm hoping to catch the opposition uawares over this weekend. I know those multi-corporation types—Monday-to-Friday men, every one of them!' he added with a scornful short bark of grim laughter. 'So I've arranged for a whistle-stop tour around the country houses of some influential contacts, and there are one or two long-standing debts and favours due to me that I'm going to call in over this weekend.'

'What about your businesses in Australia? If they aren't part of your main holding company in London, maybe you could use them to set up some sort of diversion?' she queried.

Ross turned his dark head to give her a broad smile of approval. 'Clever girl! Let's hope the opposition aren't quite as bright as you seem to be,' he said, his words and the warmth of his smile suddenly bringing a flush to her cheeks. 'Actually I'm keeping the Australian connection in reserve for what I hope will be a final, knock-out blow,' Ross added, before snapping shut the locks on his suitcase and lifting it off the bed.

'Ross—I do wish that. . .' she began, hoping even at this last moment for some word, some sign that the scorching, torrid passion that had exploded between them in the Hamptons had meant as much to him as it had to her.

But the opportunity was lost as he placed an arm lightly about her shoulders, giving her a quick peck on the cheek and saying, 'Look after yourself, Laura, and don't worry about the twins. I'm sure you won't have any problems,' before striding off through the living-room, and banging the front door closed behind him.

No problems. . .? Laura almost groaned out loud as she recalled Ross's reassuring words when he'd left for London two days ago. In fact, she didn't just feel like groaning—the frustration and worry she felt at the moment were enough to make her want to scream blue murder!

But it was obvious that giving way, by either yelling or dissolving into tears, wasn't going to get her anywhere in this awful place. It was up to her to get herself and the twins out of here, back to the safety of their apartment—and clearly any display of outrage or temperament was only going to delay matters.

Placing her hands on her knees to try to stop them trembling, Laura sat upright in her chair on the other side of the table from the two hard-faced men in blue uniforms. Casting a despairing glance around at the stark walls of the interview-room in the police station, she took a deep unsteady breath. 'But I really *have* told you the truth,' she said as firmly as she could.

'So tell us again, lady,' one of the policemen demanded roughly.

'Well. . . I was just taking the children for a walk in the park. It was such a hot day; the air-conditioning had broken down, yet again, and the twins were nearly going mad at being cooped up in the hot apartment. So I decided to take them outside for a breath of fresh air,' she added, turning her worried blue eyes in mute appeal to the uniformed policewoman sitting in the corner of the room.

'Yeah, yeah,' one of the men in front of her muttered impatiently. 'So what happened next?'

Laura gave a heavy sigh. 'Quite honestly—it wasn't much cooler in the park. I was feeling so tired that I just sank down on to a bench, and——'

'Oh—for God's sake, get on with it!'

'But that's the whole point,' Laura protested. '*I* was sitting on the bench while the children ran off to play. And it wasn't until about five minutes later that one of the twins—and I honestly don't know which, because they keep swapping their headbands. . .' she explained.

But, when she saw one of the tough, huge policemen casting his eyes up to the ceiling in exasperation, she hurriedly continued her story.

'Anyway, one of the children was carrying this plastic bag, containing what looked like icing sugar. And when I asked her what she was doing with it, Emma—or maybe it was Sophie—told me that it had been dropped by two men, who were fighting each other behind some trees on the other side of the park.'

'But surely you must have known——?'

'No—of course I didn't!' Laura snapped. 'How in the world would *I* know it was a bag of cocaine? I've never seen any of the horrid stuff in my whole life! And I *definitely* think that taking drugs is disgusting. Anyone who sells them is thoroughly evil and should be sent to prison immediately!' she added forcefully.

'Yeah—that's what we think, too,' the senior policeman told her menacingly.

Laura gulped nervously. 'Well, anyway. . .the last thing I wanted to do was to get involved in a fight—especially as I had the children with me. So I told them that we were going to leave the park, and go and get a nice cold ice-cream. We were just walking away, and I was looking for some sort of rubbish container in which to put the bag of icing sugar, when we suddenly heard all those sirens going, and saw masses of policemen running into the park. And. . .well, you know the rest,' she added lamely.

'Humph. . .' the policeman grunted, staring down at the notes before him. 'It looks as if we've got you for resisting arrest as well,' he told her grimly.

'What did you expect?' she retorted quickly. 'Those great bully-boys of yours were insisting on dragging me away from the children, who were crying and practically having hysterics in the midst of all that noise and shouting. And where *are* the children?' she demanded angrily. 'Those poor little girls must be frightened out of their minds! And if you don't let me go—right this minute!—I'm going to get straight in touch with the

British Embassy, and. . .and anyone else I can think of!' she added furiously.

'Hey—cool down, lady,' the other policeman warned. 'For your information, those "poor little girls" of yours are having the time of their lives playing tag around our office. And not only have they consumed practically a quart of maple ice-cream, but just before I came in here they were ordering some pizzas! Right?' he added, turning to wink at the policewoman across the room.

'Right!' she agreed with a grin.

'I really don't like them eating that sort of disgusting junk food,' Laura protested.

The policeman gave a harsh laugh. 'Believe me, lady,' he said as he and his companion rose to their feet, 'that's the very *least* of your problems!'

As the men went out of the door Laura stared glumly over at the young policewoman. What on earth was she going to do? *Thank God Ross was in England*! With any luck she might be able to get back to the apartment before he found out what had happened. And nothing *would* have happened if Angelique had started work yesterday, as she'd promised. Unfortunately the wretched girl had never even turned up. And when Laura had contacted the person who'd written one of the glowing references the woman on the other end of the phone hadn't sounded at all surprised. Sighing helplessly, she'd merely said, 'If you don't give these girls a terrific reference they're likely to turn around and sue you in the courts for defamation of character!'

Since there had been clearly nothing she could do about the situation, Laura had been forced to buckle down and do what she could to keep the twins happy.

She'd been ashamed to find that she found it such exhausting work, especially without the broad shoulders of Ross to lean on. Not only was he going to be absolutely furious about her being in this police station, but she dreaded having to tell her cousin about it too.

When she and the twins had visited the hospital this morning Laura had been upset to note that Liz had seemed to be deeply depressed. Not that her cousin's health had relapsed, or anything like that, but her mood had communicated itself to the twins, who'd been particularly fractious and difficult. In some extraordinary manner the children seemed better able to cope with their parents' injuries when they were well away from the hospital. Maybe seeing their mother and father in such pain was having a bad effect on the little girls?

Obviously Laura was worried about Liz's lack of progress, but for the immediate present—here and now—she was primarily concerned about what was going to happen next. They couldn't keep them here all night—or could they? Biting her lip with worry, and trying not to give way to her feelings of fear and trepidation, she looked up quickly as the door opened.

'OK, lady—you're free to go.'

'Really?' She jumped quickly to her feet. 'You're not going to charge me—or anything like that?'

'No. Just get the hell out of here—and take those two little devils with you!' the policeman told her with a surprisingly friendly laugh. 'We're prepared to accept that you just got caught up in a drug bust. But the next time you see a bag of "icing sugar" lying around I suggest that you *don't* pick it up!' he added with heavy sarcasm.

Laura was so relieved that she could only nod silently while she followed him out of the room. And then, to her almost inexpressible joy, she caught sight of a familiar tall, broad-shouldered figure across the crowded main office of the station.

'*Ross*. . .!' she cried, running over and throwing herself into his arms. 'Oh, Ross! You've no *idea* what's been happening to us!' she said, before suddenly bursting into a storm of tears.

'Oh, yes, I have! How could you be such a damn stupid fool?' he demanded as, despite his harsh words, his strong arms closed reassuringly about her trembling figure. 'I can't leave you alone for five minutes, can I?' he added, taking out a large white handkerchief and carefully wiping the tears from her eyes. 'I reckon that it's definitely about time that we went home.'

'Yes. . .yes. . .please!' she muttered, blinking tearfully up at him. 'I never thought I would be glad to see that apartment again, but I can hardly wait to get home.'

'I didn't mean the apartment,' he drawled as the twins came dancing happily across the office towards them. 'When I said "home" I meant that we're all going back home—to London!'

CHAPTER NINE

LAURA sighed, leaning back on the hard bench and gazing up at the overcast sky.

'I do wish it were a bit warmer,' she muttered, shivering as the fresh, light breeze ruffled her blonde hair.

'You're never satisfied!' Julie laughed. 'You have just been telling me about the steamy heat of New York in summer—and *now* you're moaning about the cold weather here in London!'

'Yes, well. . .' Laura gave her friend a shamefaced grin. 'I really am glad to be home, even if it means having to put up with a typical British summer. It's just a bit difficult to get used to the startling contrast, that's all. . . *Hey!* Don't go too near the water!' she called out before leaping to her feet and running over to where the twins were feeding some ducks at the edge of the Serpentine.

'It's a lot deeper than it looks,' she cautioned the children. 'So watch it—OK?'

'We'll be very careful,' Emma promised her.

Laura smiled down at the little girl, whom she now found no difficulty in telling apart from her twin, Sophie. 'I know you will, honey,' she murmured, fondly brushing the pale blonde curls from the child's brow before walking slowly back to rejoin her friend.

'It's ages since I've been to Hyde Park. I'm surprised

to find it so quiet and peaceful,' Julie said as Laura sat down on the bench once more. 'And the twins are *so* sweet,' she added, giving an almost envious sigh as she watched the two children, each with her own brown paper bag, busy feeding stale bread to the ducks.

'Yes, they're adorable—but they can be little demons as well,' Laura laughed. 'We come here most days. Although I must admit that to begin with I was a bit twitchy about taking the kids to a park—even here in London.'

'I'm not surprised!' the other girl agreed sympathetically, having just heard from Laura the full story of her traumatic outing, which had culminated in her being arrested and ending up in the New York police station. 'You must have been so relieved when Ross turned up and it was all sorted out.'

'You can say that again!' Laura exclaimed fervently.

Julie frowned slightly. 'What I don't quite understand. . . I mean, I know you said the children's parents are still in hospital, but they must miss the twins. And the children can't find it easy to be so far away from their mother. I don't want to speak out of turn, of course, but. . .'

'It's all right—I wasn't at all happy about the arrangements either,' Laura agreed, before explaining that when Ross had returned to New York he'd gone straight to the hospital from the airport, before eventually returning to the empty apartment. Worried by their absence, it was only when he had contacted the superintendent of the building—who seemed to know everything that happened in the neighbourhood—that he'd learned exactly what had happened to Laura and the twins.

And it was apparently during that hospital visit that Ross and his brother had had a long serious talk about what would be best for the children.

'The twins were, quite naturally, upset when they first saw their parents again after the accident,' Laura explained. 'Although Owen managed to cope with the problem quite well, Liz got really depressed—which further upset the children. A sort of catch-twenty-two or chick-and-egg situation, if you see what I mean,' she told Julie. 'And so, after having a good, long talk about the problem with both Liz and Owen, Ross decided that it would be best if we brought the girls back here, to London, until their parents leave hospital.'

'Your poor cousin. She must miss the children quite dreadfully,' Julie murmured.

'Yes, she does,' Laura agreed sadly. 'But it turned out that Liz was also desperately worried about how she and Owen were going to manage to pay the *huge* hospital bills. But, now she knows that Ross has insisted on taking care of everything, Liz is beginning to make very good progress. Quite honestly,' Laura added, 'I think she's finding it easier, somehow, to concentrate on getting well—as quickly as possible—without having to worry too much about Emma and Sophie. They phone her every day, of course, and I'm sure it won't be long before the whole family is reunited once again.'

'And so you're all staying at Lady Wyndham's house in Lowndes Square? How are you getting on with the old battleaxe?' Julie grinned, recalling her friend's difficult relationship with her elderly mother-in-law.

'Don't ask!' Laura groaned. 'I could almost *weep* when I think how pleased I was to be returning to England. Goodness knows, I've never liked the woman—but I'd no idea just how awful living in her house would turn out to be. It's *horrendous*!'

Julie giggled. 'It can't be as bad as all that, surely?'

'Oh, yes, it is!' Laura told her with a heavy sigh. 'I know that old Sir David only died last year—just before my own father—and I realise that she must be worried sick about poor Owen. But, even making all the allowances I can, she is still *totally* impossible! Half of the trouble, of course, is that she always had nannies for her own children. So she has absolutely no idea how to cope with young children.

'Quite frankly,' Laura continued, 'if I hear her say, "I really don't know *why* you can't keep the twins quiet," in that scathing upper-class voice of hers just once more I swear I'm going to hit the old bat!'

Julie gave a peal of laughter. 'You should try looking after my class of twelve-year-old juvenile delinquents!'

'I thought you were supposed to be my friend. . .?' Laura grumbled. 'And, anyway, it's all right for *you*— you've got the school holidays to look forward to. Incidentally,' she added with a frown, 'I thought you were going to Greece this summer.'

'Yes, I was. But it all fell through at the last moment. So I'm a lady of leisure for the next six weeks!'

'Lucky old you!' Laura sighed.

'Well, you are too—more or less,' her friend pointed out. 'What about your job? Is your boss still being sympathetic about your problems, or is he itching to get you back to the office?'

'A bit of both, I suppose,' Laura shrugged. 'The work is obviously piling up, and there's always the worry that my clients might get cheesed off and take their business elsewhere. Tim Dunton has been very kind, of course,' she added with a sigh. 'But he's been a bit grumpy about the reappearance of Ross in my life, and the fact that I'm having to live with my mother-in-law.'

'Since he wants to marry you himself, I'm not at all surprised,' Julie told her. 'However, I wouldn't mind living in a huge London house in Knightsbridge, and being waited on by all those servants. There are worse fates in life, you know.'

'Yes, it sounds all right—but the reality is *very* different,' Laura retorted grimly. 'The beastly old woman has told me, quite bluntly, that she considers me very much an *ex*-wife. And that the sooner Ross gets a divorce, the happier she'll be. In fact, right from the first moment we arrived back in London she's done her best to make my life absolute hell!'

'I didn't realise the situation was so bad!' Julie murmured with concern. 'Can't you get Ross to do something about it?'

'I would if I could—but he's been flying back and forth to Australia like a damned Yo-Yo! I've hardly even *seen* the man, let alone managed to have five minutes' conversation with him.'

Laura lapsed into a glum silence, staring blindly over at the children, who were now sitting on the grass, busily trying to make daisy chains.

She hadn't told Julie about her hopes for a reconciliation with Ross—nor, of course, about the fact that they'd made love to each other. So how could she possibly tell her friend about the almost wild grief she felt at the prolonged absence of her husband; the deep, stabbing pain in her heart when she remembered their wonderful night of passion? All of which made it impossible to explain exactly why she'd been so upset to find, after arriving, tired and exhausted, at the large house in Lowndes Square, that she was going to see even less of Ross than she had in New York?

All four of them had been thoroughly jet-lagged. So it had seemed sensible for Ross to have his old bedroom, while she'd been far too weary to care *where* she slept. But, on getting her act together later the next day, Laura had been appalled to discover that not only had Ross already left for Australia—but she'd been given a small attic room next to the children's nursery.

Laura suddenly startled Julie as she gave a shrill, unhappy laugh. 'You won't believe it, but my dear mother-in-law has shoved me permanently up in the attic with the children, *and* we're expected to stay up there all the time. I've been banned from the rest of the house—just as if I had some awful contagious disease!'

'I can hardly believe that——'

'I'm not kidding!' Laura ground out bitterly. 'Honestly, Julie, Lady Wyndham behaves as though Queen Victoria were still on the throne. She even talks about "the lower orders" when she's referring to her servants. And that's not all! When I was out with the children the other day she took a call from Tim Dunton. When she learned—shock, horror, dismay!—that he wanted to take me out to dinner she had the brass nerve to call me "a Jezebel"! Can you beat it?'

'Oh, dear! Poor Laura!' Julie murmured, struggling not to laugh.

'It's not funny. I thought I'd at least get some sympathy from *you*,' Laura moaned, suddenly feeling that the whole world was against her.

'I'm not being unsympathetic,' the other girl assured her earnestly. 'But I can't see why you're putting up with such nonsense. If Ross isn't around to deal with his awful mother, and if your life in her house is so unbearable, why don't you and the kids move into our apartment in Wapping?'

'I'd already thought of that,' Laura told her gloomily. 'But when I mentioned it to Ross, during the flight from America, he was dead against the idea. Mainly because it hasn't got a garden for the children to play in,' she explained. 'Although there's not much joy for them in the one at his mother's, which is mostly terraced with hard stone flags, and "my precious flowers", which mustn't be touched.'

The other girl shrugged. 'Well, I'd have thought the solution was obvious. You've got that large house and garden down in Devon, haven't you? Why don't you take the children there? Mr and Mrs Bryant would be thrilled to have a family living in your old home once again—and, since my holiday plans have fallen through, I'd be happy to come down and help you with the twins.'

'That's a terrific idea. . .' Laura said slowly, her sapphire-blue eyes beginning to sparkle as she realised that it might, just possibly, be the answer to her problems. And then her face fell. 'But it wouldn't work. Ross would be sure to object. I can't see him allowing me take the children so far away from London.'

'Well, it's worth asking him—isn't it?'

Laura shrugged, and gave a heavy sigh. 'Yes, it might be, *if* I could get hold of him. But, as he's still somewhere in Australia—and goodness knows when he'll return—I don't rate my chances too highly.'

'Hang on a minute—Ross is only the twins' uncle,' Julie pointed out. 'You've just told me that the girls phone their mother every night. So if you had a word with Liz I bet she'd be delighted to give you permission for the kids to visit the old family home.'

'Hey—that's a bit sneaky, isn't it?' Laura exclaimed. 'If I went behind his back like that Ross would be absolutely *furious*!' she added with a nervous gurgle of laughter.

'I expect you're right!' Julie agreed solemnly, having difficulty in keeping a straight face.

'But it would be the solution to my problems, wouldn't it. . .?' Laura said slowly.

'It would certainly be a lot better than your present situation,' Julie agreed, glancing down at her watch. 'Oops—I'll have to go. I was supposed to meet a friend in Harrods five minutes ago.'

Walking back through the park, and carefully holding the children's hands as they crossed the busy road, Laura found it almost impossible to ignore her friend's sly suggestion.

She felt almost overwhelmed by a deep physical longing to leave this busy city—and the increasing tension of her life in Lady Wyndham's house. Her mind filled with pictures of the old grey-stone manor house, surrounded by peaceful green fields, where the children could run and play to their hearts' content. But it was no good. Even leaving aside Ross's anger at not being consulted about such an important decision, it would be irresponsible to put her own needs and desires above those of the children.

Besides, she was ultimately responsible to Liz for the twins' welfare, Laura firmly reminded herself as they mounted the wide steps up to the front door of Lady Wyndham's house. And, while Emma and Sophie were still happy here in London, she had no alternative but to try and endure the venomous pin-pricks of her elderly mother-in-law.

Laura walked slowly through the open french windows, out on to the stone terrace. Gazing idly over the rolling green lawns, she watched the red glow of the sun, slowly beginning to sink down over the horizon. They had been down here in Devon for almost two weeks, and already she had fallen under the lazy, carefree spell of the tranquil countryside. In the distance she could hear the rumble of a local farmer's combine, busily gathering in this year's corn harvest, while from an upstairs window floated the happy laughter of Emma and Sophie, mingling with the busy hum of bees in the nearby lime trees.

'It's my turn to bath the kids,' Julie had said firmly when they'd returned early this evening from spending the day on a nearby beach. 'You haven't exactly had a peaceful birthday!' she'd reminded Laura, who'd smiled as she had recalled the twins' boundless energy, which had left the two adults feeling quite exhausted at the end of the day. 'And besides,' Julie had added, looking at her friend with concern, 'you aren't looking too well. Are you sure you feel all right?'

'Yes, I'm fine,' Laura had told her quickly, nervously changing the subject before Julie could probe any further.

Walking slowly up and down the old stone terrace, Laura tried to empty her mind—to banish the sick feelings of fear and apprehension which had haunted her during the last week.

It would be far better to count her blessings, she told herself firmly. And it *was* wonderful to have heard from Liz today, when her cousin had rung to wish her a happy birthday, that she was expected to be discharged from hospital in about a week's time.

Despite being confined to her bed in the hospital in New York, Liz had been an absolute tower of strength over Laura's sudden departure from London. It had been her cousin's whole-hearted approval—and her joy at the thought of her children returning to the old family home—that had given Laura the courage to leave her mother-in-law's house in Knightsbridge.

Only two days after meeting Julie by the Serpentine in Hyde Park matters had come very quickly to a head. Because, while she could just about put up with the attitude of Lady Wyndham towards herself, there was no way she was prepared to let the beastly old woman be unkind to the children. And seeing Lady Wyndham viciously slapping poor Sophie around the face when the little girl—after eating too much ice-cream—had been sick all over the priceless Aubusson carpet in the drawing-room had finally decided the matter, as far as Laura was concerned.

After comforting the little girl and brushing away her tears, Laura had taken the children upstairs to the nursery. And then, waiting until her mother-in-law had left the house for a game of bridge with some of her friends, Laura had gone downstairs to telephone her cousin in New York.

'You're absolutely right!' Liz had said, sounding strong, healthy and extremely indignant at the way her child had been treated. 'I think taking them to Devon is a *great* idea,' she'd enthused. 'The kids will love it there. And I hope they have as much fun as we used to when we were younger.'

'So I've got your full permission to take them away?' Laura had asked her.

'You certainly have! And Owen's too, for that matter,' Liz had told her firmly. 'I know he'll be very angry with his mother—he's always hated the thought of anyone being rough with his children. In fact, if *I'd* been there I would have given the wretched old woman a hefty slap myself—just to see how *she* liked it!'

Despite the seriousness of the situation, Laura had been forced to laugh. 'Don't worry! As soon as she hit poor little Sophie Emma immediately rushed over and kicked her grandmother hard in the shins! In the end, our dear mother-in-law was yelling louder than the children!'

Liz's gurgle of laughter had floated down the wires. 'I know I shouldn't say it—but well done, Emma! So go ahead and take the children down to Devon, Laura. And don't worry—I'm completely confident of your ability to look after them properly.'

Laura had been pleased and reassured to hear her cousin's vote of confidence. And after phoning Julie, who had agreed to join her in Devon, she'd also been heartened by her friend's confirmation that she was doing the right thing.

Lady Wyndham had not taken the decision at all well, and the scene which had followed was one that Laura preferred to forget. However, there was nothing the elderly woman could have done to prevent her departure with the two children, who had been clearly delighted to be leaving their grandmother's house. Although whether her mother-in-law would actually give Ross the letter she'd left for him, she had no idea.

Laura had never had any doubts that she'd made the right decision. The children had bloomed in the soft Devonshire air, completely winning the heart of Mrs Bryant, even if they drove Mr Bryant wild by sneaking into the kitchen garden and eating all his prize raspberries!

Julie, too, had been clearly delighted to return to the countryside of her childhood. And, after being out in the sunshine with the children most of the day, she'd lost her pale, city complexion, becoming as brown as a berry and looking much younger.

Even her best friends would never have said that Julie was a particularly pretty girl, but the fresh glowing skin and sparkling green eyes of the dark-haired girl seemed to have caught the notice of the local doctor.

Laura smiled to herself as she remembered their visit to his surgery when one of the children had cut a foot on some glass. Always used to receiving admiring glances from men, Laura hadn't known whether to be pleased or not when the doctor had completely ignored her— clearly having eyes only for Julie. And he certainly hadn't let the grass grow under his feet! He'd taken her out to dinner that very night, and now seemed to be practically haunting the place, and obviously very much in love with her friend.

Julie herself was being far more cautious. 'He does seem very nice,' she'd murmured this morning, her cheeks flushed after receiving a phone call from the doctor.

'What do you mean by "nice"?' Laura had demanded. 'Don't be so mealy-mouthed—you know that you're crazy about him!' she'd added, smiling as the colour had deepened on her friend's face. 'As far as I can see, you two are made for each other!'

Which was more than you could say for her and Ross, Laura thought miserably. She'd been so certain that he would have contacted her by now. His long, inexplicable silence had resulted in her feeling such misery that she was finding it difficult to eat or sleep. She seemed unable to prevent herself from going over in her mind every single minute of the days they had spent together in America. And now she knew that she would have done anything to be able to roll back the clock.

Given another chance, she wouldn't have let her stupid pride or injured dignity become a barrier between them. If she'd taken her courage in both hands, and told him of her true feelings, they might have had a chance to work something out. It would have been far better to have at least made the attempt—even if it might have ended in disaster—than be left with such intense regrets and nostalgia for what might have been.

Everything seemed to remind her of him: the jade T-shirt which she'd worn on that happy day they'd spent on the beach; a phrase of music on the radio which they'd listened to together; and even baking a chocolate cake for the children had almost broken her up when she'd remembered how much he'd enjoyed the one she had made in New York.

The whole situation seemed both tragic and also profoundly humiliating—as when she'd picked up one of his sweaters, packed in her suitcase by mistake. She hadn't been able to prevent herself from burying her face in the soft wool—and almost groaning out loud in agony as she'd inhaled the strongly male, musky scent of his cologne.

Brushing a trembling hand through her hair, Laura squirmed with embarrassment. How could her obviously unrequited love have brought her to such a low, pathetic state? But she *must* try and pull herself together. Because it wasn't just Ross's non-appearance that was causing her such distress. The awful discovery that she'd missed her last period and that, following their night of love and passion she was now probably expecting his baby was making Ross's silence almost unbearably hard to accept. She couldn't even begin to contemplate the future—the present was bad enough. However, clearly the problem was not going to go away, and she would have to face the harsh reality of a pregnancy, and single motherhood in the future, very soon.

Her deeply unhappy thoughts were interrupted as Julie came out on the terrace to join her.

'The twins have had their bath. They're now sitting up in bed, waiting for their aunt to give them a kiss— and looking like little angels,' Julie told her, adding with a grin, 'which, of course, they aren't!'

'I'll go up and hear their prayers in a minute,' Laura

said, managing to summon up a smile as she gazed at her friend. 'You're looking very smart. And I like the colour of your dress—you ought to wear that particular shade of red more often.'

Julie's cheeks flushed with pleasure at the compliment. 'Are you sure you don't mind me leaving you tonight? It *is* your birthday, after all, and I don't have to go out to dinner. I'm sure that——'

'Nonsense!' Laura told her firmly. 'Quite honestly— and who wants to celebrate becoming twenty-six?—I'm really looking forward to a long soak in the bath, and then putting my feet up in front of the TV,' she added firmly. 'It's been a long day, and I'm feeling quite tired.'

'Yes, you look it,' Julie told her bluntly.

Wishing that her friend were sometimes not *quite* so outspoken, Laura suppressed a small sigh before they heard the noise of wheels crunching on gravel, and a car horn being tooted impatiently.

'I'd better go,' Julie said, coming over to give the taller girl a quick hug. 'Enjoy your nice, quiet evening— and don't worry, Ross is bound to be getting in touch with you, very soon,' she added softly, before running off to answer yet another imperative toot on the horn.

Later, as she walked slowly downstairs, only a light blue silk dressing-gown over her skin, which was still warm and fragrant from the bath oil, Laura realised that she really didn't want to watch any television. It was a lovely warm evening, and as she drifted across the drawing-room she felt a sudden impulse to play some music. Sitting down at her mother's old grand piano, she lifted the lid of the keyboard. It was years since she'd played, of course, and her fingers were bound to be rusty, but she couldn't resist trying out some of the pieces of music she used to play so long ago.

It was hard going at first, but after a while her hands began to flow over the keys in an easier, more assured style, and Laura found that she was able to relax, the soft chords and harmony having a soothing effect on her lacerated emotions.

Maybe Julie was right, after all. Her friend's well-known bluntness had been to the fore a few days ago, when she'd discovered Laura sobbing quietly in her bedroom. Unable to keep up the pretence any longer, she'd told her friend the whole, disastrous story behind her stay in New York, only withholding her fears about a possible pregnancy as she'd related the disastrous sequence of events.

'Any relationship between two Leos is fraught with problems,' Julie had told her, firmly ignoring Laura's groan of protest at her friend's obsession with star signs.

'There can only be *one* king of the castle, as far as male Leos are concerned,' Julie had continued. 'And unless you're going to allow it to be your husband—to let him be boss, in fact—your relationship is never going to work. But, for heaven's sake, Laura, you're a clever woman. I'm sure you're quite capable of getting your own way, while letting Ross think that he's calling the shots!'

Smiling reluctantly through her tears, Laura had shaken her head. 'There's much more to it than that. I've always felt that he ought to *know* how I'm feeling— to realise that I've got problems too. Forcing me to make that dreadful decision when we were first married—to either go abroad with him, or look after my father—was something I've always found terribly hard to forgive. It was just *so* unreasonable!' she'd moaned as the tears had begun flowing again.

'Well, you were both much younger then, of course,' Julie had said comfortingly. 'I'm sure that he'd never make the same mistake again. Unfortunately, being a typical Leo, he'd have stuck to his guns—even if he was as miserable and unhappy as you were. But he was too proud—just like you!—to admit that he was in the wrong.'

'But surely we ought to have been able to find some sort of compromise. . .' Laura had begun, pausing as Julie had given a hoot of laughter.

'I bet Ross's idea of compromise is for you to do what *he* wants! And he is not going to be too keen on you continuing with your career, either,' she'd added warningly.

Laura had shrugged. 'I honestly don't care about that,' she'd told her friend. 'I've reached the top of my profession, and am almost getting too old for the job, anyway. But it's no good. I'm sure that he won't——'

'If he hasn't contacted you there must be a good reason why not,' Julie had said firmly. 'And when he does—why not be totally honest? All you have to do, Laura, is to tell him that you love him,' she'd added, putting her arms around her old friend and giving her a hug. 'I know that's terribly difficult for a Leo lady to do, but it *must* be worth it— especially if it means a lifetime of happiness.'

Now, as her fingers moved smoothly over the piano keys, Laura acknowledged that Julie was right. Her friend had been so perceptive about the complicated, tortuous relationship between herself and Ross that maybe there really *was* something in astrology, after all?

Immersed in her thoughts, she was surprised to hear through the open french windows the sound of a car engine. Surely it was too early for Julie to be returning from her dinner date? Hoping that nothing had gone wrong with the course of her friend's romance, she turned around on the piano stool as she heard hard, firm footsteps walking along the terrace.

A moment later she almost fainted as Ross walked calmly into the room.

CHAPTER TEN

HER sapphire-blue eyes wide with shock, her whole body shaking with tension as if in the grip of a raging fever, Laura stared across the room at her husband. As Ross came to a halt just inside the open french windows, their silk curtains billowing softly in the light breeze, the dark evening sky outside provided a dramatic background to his tall, broad-shouldered figure.

Fighting to control her ragged breathing, Laura gazed at his expressionless face, which gave her no clue to what he was thinking as he regarded her intently from beneath his heavy eyelids.

In the long silence that stretched between them she could almost hear her heart pounding like a sledgehammer in her chest. And then, as her dazed mind finally absorbed the fact that it really *was* Ross, and not a figment of her overheated imagination, she quickly jumped to her feet and ran swiftly across the floor towards him.

'Happy Birthday, Laura!'

'*Ross*. . .!' she cried, throwing herself into his arms and tearfully clinging to his broad shoulders. 'Oh, Ross—p-please don't. . .don't *ever* leave me again!'

For the length of a heartbeat his tall figure remained stiff and unyielding, and then she heard him swear harshly under his breath, and felt his strong arms enfolding her trembling figure.

167

'Laura, darling!' he murmured as he gathered her more tightly into his warm embrace. 'There's no need to cry.'

'Oh, Ross. . .' she sobbed, clasping her hands about his neck, burying her fingers in his thick dark hair. 'I. . . I've been *such* a fool!'

'No—no, my darling,' he sighed. 'It's I who have been a fool—for five intolerable, hideously long years,' he added softly, gently wiping the tears from her eyes before covering her upturned face with butterfly-light kisses that made her heart sing for joy.

'But you don't understand!' She sniffed, her trembling body still shaken by occasional sobs. 'I. . . I let my stupid pride come between us. I did so want to tell you how I felt, but I just. . .just couldn't seem to, somehow. Oh, Ross—I've been so stupid, and I love you *so* much,' she whispered, burying her face in his shoulder.

'*Laura*. . .!' She could feel the breath being slowly expelled from his powerful body in a long-drawn-out emotional sigh. 'My darling Laura. . .' his voice was thick and husky with emotion. . .'when I fell fathoms deep in love with you—all those years ago—you captured my heart for all time. And nothing that has happened to us since then. . .neither our separation, nor misguided, foolish pride on both our parts. . .*nothing* can ever change or alter my deep love for you.'

'Oh, Ross. . .those are the most. . .the most romantic words I've *ever* heard!' she whispered, tears of happiness streaming down her pale cheeks. 'I. . . I never stopped loving you, either. . .however hard I tried to fool myself that I had. . .'

'Don't cry, my sweet. Please don't. . .' he murmured,

holding her tightly in his arms and kissing away her tears.

'It's just. . .' she smiled tremulously at him through damp, spiky eyelashes '. . .it's just that I can't. . . I really can't believe it's possible to feel so happy!' She lifted a hand to touch his cheek in wonder and joy as he smiled tenderly down at her.

'I hope to spend the rest of my life convincing you, every day, how very much I love you,' he said thickly, gazing down into her lovely face. 'Starting right now, this minute. . .' he murmured softly, brushing her lips delicately with his mouth, before quickly sweeping her lightly gowned figure up in his arms and carrying her towards the door.

With an ecstatic sigh of deep happiness Laura nestled her head in the hollow of his broad shoulder, only his low, mocking laugh managing to break through her state of utter bliss.

'Darling. . . I haven't a clue about the layout of this house, so you're going to have to point me in the right direction!'

'Hmm. . .?'

'Come on—you idiot! Where's the bedroom?' he demanded roughly as he carried her up the wide curving staircase.

'Shush! For heaven's sake, Ross—you'll wake the children!' she whispered, raising a trembling finger to his lips, as they reached the landing. 'There's no need to———.'

'There's every need—because I'm a desperate man!' he growled savagely in her ear. 'Not *only* have I been separated from my wife for the past five years—but in all that time I've only *once* managed to make love to her. So if you don't want to be hung, drawn and quartered,' he added menacingly through clenched teeth, 'You'd better point out your bedroom—*right this minute*!'

'OK, OK. . .keep your hair on!' she muttered, secretly thrilled at the fierce, fiery passion in his voice as she waved towards a door.

'It's about all I *am* intending to keep on!' he told her with a husky, sensual bark of laughter that left her breathless and quivering in his arms as he entered the room and tossed her lightly down on to the bed.

There was a long, emotionally charged silence as they stared at one another, before he began to roughly shrug the jacket from his broad shoulders. She shivered, suddenly feeling ridiculously shy and uncertain for a moment as he swiftly unknotted his tie and quickly removed his shirt with tense movements.

Her slender body trembled helplessly as she lay gazing up at his tall, lithe figure, her normally pale cheeks covered by a hectic flush of rising excitement. And then, unable to bear the silence and tension any longer, she raised her slim arms towards him. 'Ross. . .?' Her soft whisper was an innocent enticement, a tempting siren song that he couldn't resist.

'*Laura*!' he groaned, tossing aside his shirt and swiftly divesting himself of his clothes before lying down on the bed beside her. 'My love. . .' he breathed thickly, his strong, tanned fingers sweeping open her gown to reveal the swollen, thrusting peaks of her breasts beneath the thin silk. His husky moan of arousal as she placed her hands on his warm chest shattered the last remnants of any uncertainty she might have felt, and her arms closed about him as she revelled in the hard pressure of Ross's body, the slight roughness of his masculine jaw as her silk gown was torn away and he pressed his burning lips to the soft, fragrant valley between her full breasts.

Carried away on a rushing tide of dark enchantment, she quivered as his tongue caressed her skin, his mouth feather-light as it brushed enticingly, back and forth, over her swollen nipples. Moaning helplessly, her sapphire-blue eyes darkening with overwhelming desire and need, she gasped as his lips closed hungrily over one hard rosy peak, the increasingly erotic touch of his mouth and tongue producing a sudden clench of rippling sensations deep in her stomach. Her body arched pleadingly beneath him as she reached up, trailing her lips slowly over the now moist, tanned skin of his powerful chest, with its covering of rough dark hair tapering to a point on his flat stomach. A deep, husky groan broke from his throat as her soft lips followed the intimate downward path of her fingers, his body shuddering almost uncontrollably before he gathered her tightly against him, his mouth closing over her lips in an urgent, fierce statement of possession.

Slowly raising his head, Ross stared down at his wife, his grey eyes stormy with passion as he gazed at the blonde hair forming a golden halo about her head, and the creamy skin of her naked body, gleaming in the light of the soft lamps.

'You're so lovely. . .for years I've dreamed of you lying beside me like this!' he breathed thickly, his powerful body shaking with tension as he tried to control his mounting passion.

At the sound of his husky voice Laura's heart began beating rapidly, her breathing quickening, and, totally beyond her control, her body began moving sensually and invitingly beneath him. He trembled and groaned as her hands moved urgently over his flesh, before drawing her roughly against the pulsating length of him, letting her feel his arousal, his mouth moving blindly over her soft velvety skin, touching and tasting, raising her senses to such a pitch that she cried out, the wild clamouring in her blood, the driving need for his possession more than she could bear.

An intense heat spread through her quivering, eager figure, and she rejoiced in the overwhelmingly sensual pleasure of their entwined bodies, welcoming the deep, shuddering thrust of his virile manhood. And then all conscious thought was obliterated as an urgent, tingling excitement contracted through her body, and she was soaring free with him into realms of exquisite delight, where their hearts and souls became one.

'You see—we didn't wake the children, after all,' Ross drawled, his eyes glinting with amusement as he gazed warmly down at the soft figure in his arms.

'They might have had a good sleep—but we certainly haven't!' Laura gave a low gurgle of laughter as she snuggled closer to him. 'You're simply insatiable!'

'Really. . .?' he drawled, raising a dark eyebrow as his fingertips idly drew patterns on her soft, yielding flesh.

'Really!' She grinned, recalling how they seemed to have spent most of the night making love—time and again.

'Are you having the nerve to complain because I can't

keep my hands off your wonderful body?' he growled with mock-ferocity.

'No—I definitely am not!' she sighed happily, unable to say any more as his mouth possessed her lips in a long, slow, lingering kiss. 'Strewth!' Laura gasped breathlessly as he raised his dark head, gazing fondly up at the man she loved so much. 'But I suppose we ought to be sensible and try to get some sleep,' she added reluctantly. 'Because the twins are bound to wake us at the crack of dawn.'

'I was glad to hear that the children are well and happy—and having the time of their lives down here in Devon. Liz says——'

'Liz? Have you been in touch with her? She never said anything about it to me.' Laura frowned.

Ross smiled down at her. 'Of course I have. You don't think that I would have left you alone, down here, if I hadn't known that you were all well and happy, do you? In fact, I've just flown back from the States today, and you'll be glad to hear that the doctors assured me that Liz and Owen are on the road to a full recovery.'

Laura sighed thankfully. 'I'm so pleased,' she told him with a beaming smile. 'Will they both be able to leave hospital next week?'

'Yes, and I hope you're going to approve, because I've made arrangements for them to come and stay here. This house is obviously a perfect place for them to both recover their strength and be reunited with the twins, whom they've missed so much.'

'Of course,' she said simply. 'We've got lots of room, and you know that I'll do anything I possibly can for them. As for the children—well, they'll be absolutely over the moon to see their parents once again.'

'I'm sorry. . .' he began, and then gave a heavy sigh. 'I'm really very sorry that I had to leave you with my mother. I now realise that it was a bad decision on my part. I didn't know. . . I had no idea how old and crotchety she'd become over the last few years.' He sighed deeply again.

'It's all right, darling,' Laura murmured, reaching up to put her slim arms about his clearly unhappy figure, and cradling his dark head against her breast. 'The twins are so happy now, which is the only thing that matters. I was just worried that you'd be furious with me for bringing them down here when you were out of the country. But, although I tried hard, I just couldn't. . .well, I'm really sorry that I couldn't cope with your mother. But that was only because you weren't there,' she added quickly, anxious to pour oil on the troubled family waters. 'I'm sure that we'll be able to get on much better in the future.'

'That's very generous of you,' he told her, raising his head to give her another slow kiss. 'And, since Owen's lectureship in the States is coming to an end and he's intending to return permanently to Britain, between the two of us we ought to be able to manage the old girl!' He gave a rueful laugh. 'I've had a few sharp, pithy words with my mother, and I don't think she'll *ever* treat her grandchildren like that again.'

'I'm sure she won't,' Laura agreed, mentally crossing her fingers and hoping that Ross proved to be right.

'Incidentally, talking about children—maybe it's time

we thought about having some of our own?' he murmured softly.

'Well. . .um. . .the fact is. . .'

'I know your career is important to you,' he said quickly. 'But I've so enjoyed looking after Emma and Sophie. I realise there's no guarantee we could have a baby straight away, of course, but——'

Laura's low, sardonic laugh cut across his words. 'That's all *you* know! The truth is. . .' She hesitated for a moment, wondering exactly how he was going to receive the news. 'The truth is, my darling husband, I'm almost sure that a baby is on the horizon—rather sooner than you think! I'm not entirely positive, of course, but, according to my arithmetic, it looks as though we "two" are about to become "three", some time in March.'

Any fears or doubts she might have had were immediately swept away by his overwhelming joy and pleasure. 'My *dearest* Laura! You wonderful, clever woman!' he exclaimed, clasping her rapturously in his arms.

She laughed softly. 'Well. . . I didn't do it *all* by myself.'

'Such modesty!' he grinned, before his expression grew more serious and determined. 'It makes all my work— everything I've fought so hard to achieve—suddenly seem worthwhile,' he told her earnestly.

'Oh, my goodness!' She gave a muffled shriek. 'I'm sorry, darling. I was so excited to see you again that I *completely* forgot to ask what's happened to your business. Did you manage to fight off the sharks?'

He smiled down at her. 'What do you think?'

'I think. . . I think you wouldn't allow *anyone* to grab hold of your business—or anything else that you possess,' she said slowly, a slight flush tingeing his cheek at her clear vote of confidence in him.

'You're quite right! I have indeed managed to frighten them away, and I don't think they'll ever try to take me on again. And, while I'm on the subject of fighting off unwanted intruders,' he added, the hard planes of his face tightening as he gazed down at her, 'I'm not prepared to allow that man Dunton to mess around with my wife any longer! When Liz told me that she thought your boss wanted to marry you I knew I had to step in and stop *that* nonsense once and for all,' he grated, his strong arms tightening possessively about her.

'Do you mean to say. . .?' she gasped. 'Are you telling me. . .that you and my sneaky cousin. . .?'

'Well, of course, I've been in touch with Liz during the last five years—how else do you think I was supposed to keep tabs on you? And Liz is married to my brother, after all. If it makes you feel any better, you may like to know that she's been telling me that our separation was all my fault—because I was too proud to climb down, or admit I was in the wrong. Believe me, your cousin doesn't mince her words,' he added ruefully. 'She was obviously anxious that we should get back together again—and, thank God, we have!' he breathed huskily.

'Oh, Ross!' she sighed. 'I was equally unhappy—how could we have let our pride and injured dignity keep us apart for so long? However, it's all very well for *you* to talk about "that man, Dunton". But what about "that girl, Marissa". . .?' she added with a sudden bitterness, her blue eyes flashing with anger as she remembered her treatment at the hands of his beautiful personal assistant.

'There's *no way* I'm prepared to accept your having anything more to do with that awful girl!'

'Darling! I can assure you——'

'She's got to go!' Laura told him fiercely. 'I don't care *how* good she is at her job. If you want our marriage to have any chance of success you'd better give her the sack first thing on Monday morning!'

Gazing down at his wife as she glared up at him, tossing back her blonde hair in an imperious gesture, Ross was suddenly reminded of a proud, possessive lioness guarding her cubs. However, this was clearly *not* the moment in which to tell his dearest Laura that she looked magnificent when she was angry, and he hastened to set the record straight.

'Relax, my darling,' he murmured soothingly, gathering her stiff figure back into his arms. 'I got rid of Marissa years ago!'

'You did. . .?' She gazed at him in blank astonishment. 'But I thought she was still working for you. I heard that she'd followed you to Sydney.'

He nodded. 'Yes, she did. But I hadn't asked her to do so, and when she began making a nuisance of herself I told her she'd have to leave our office there. So, you see, all your fears are quite groundless,' he added earnestly, taking her hand in his and raising it warmly to his lips. 'It isn't very gallant of me to say so,' he added, softly kissing her fingertips, 'but the fact is, Marissa had decided that she wanted to be the second Mrs Wyndham—while I, my darling, was only interested in the first.'

'Oh—Ross!' she breathed ecstatically, winding her arms about his neck. 'But there must have been other women during the past five years?' she murmured anxiously.

'Darling, there's never been anyone to take your place in my heart,' he vowed, the unmistakable, deeply sincere note in his voice calming her fears. 'As I hope I've just demonstrated tonight,' he grinned, 'I'm a perfectly healthy, red-blooded male. However, no one with any sense gets involved with casual sex these days; and I was simply not interested in a deeper relationship with anyone else but you. So,' he added with a slightly twisted smile, 'I just concentrated on business, and became even more of a workaholic than ever!'

'If *only* I'd been a bit more sophisticated when we first got married.' Laura gave a heavy sigh. 'Maybe I wouldn't have allowed Marissa to cause me so much unhappiness. But, when she told me about your affair with her, instead of talking it out with you I allowed it to fester in my mind.'

'I *never* had an affair with Marissa!' he protested.

'I know that *now*—but at the time I was simply too young to cope with her malice. And I hated having to give her my letters to you, but I couldn't think how else to get in touch because I didn't know your address in Australia.'

'What letters? I never received any letters from you. In fact, I was shattered when you never replied to *my* letter.' He shrugged helplessly. 'I poured out my heart to you, Laura, telling you how much I loved you, and that, despite our difficulties, I was certain we could find a way to solve them. And when you never even bothered to reply. . .' He shook his head and gave a heavy sigh.

'But Ross—I never received a letter from you! Where did you send it?'

'I didn't. I gave it to Marissa to pass on to you, and——'

'What. . .?'

They stared at each other in silence for a moment, before Laura hissed, 'It was *Marissa*! She must have destroyed both our letters! How could she have? How could she have been so. . .so treacherous? Do you realise, Ross, that she could have destroyed our lives *forever*? If Liz and Owen hadn't had that accident, which brought us together to look after the twins, we might *never* have found each other again!' she cried, feeling almost faint as she fell back on the pillows, hardly able to bear the thought of how narrowly they had averted a lifetime of unhappiness.

'If I ever see that girl again I'll kill her!' Ross ground out savagely.

'Not if I get to her first, you won't!' Laura declared, so viciously that Ross hoped his ex-personal assistant had the good sense to stay in Australia.

'However, you don't need to worry, my darling,' Ross told her firmly. 'I had already decided that we'd spent far too long apart. When I heard from Liz that your boss was starting to talk about wedding bells I swiftly moved all my operations back to London.'

'What. . .? You did that—just for me?' Laura gazed at him in open-mouthed astonishment.

A slight flush stained his cheeks. 'Well, I do have to admit that it was also a very good move businesswise,' he admitted with a laugh. 'But my intentions were very clear—and you can ask Liz if you don't believe me.'

'Of course I believe you,' she told him lovingly. 'And I can't wait to see Liz again. It will be so lovely to have her and Owen here with us. What's your brother going to do when he's fully recovered from his injuries?'

Ross hesitated for a moment. 'It's early days yet, of course. However, now that I know you're expecting a baby, I think we've got some planning to do. I'm going to be still working in the City, of course, and so I'm hoping we can live somewhere near London.'

She frowned. 'I don't see what this has got to do with Liz and Owen. And, if you want us to live nearer London, what about this house? It would be crazy to leave it empty, and I don't think I could bring myself to sell my old family home. And there's Mr and Mrs Bryant as well. Where would they go, at their time of life?'

'I've thought about that,' he told her. 'And, while I don't want to tell you what to do. . .'

'That will be the day!'

'. . .I wonder whether it might be an idea to let Liz and Owen live here with the twins?' he asked carefully. 'Owen could get a job in a nearby university—such as Exeter, for instance. So, you see, it might be the answer to all our problems.'

'I'd be happy if Liz and the twins wanted to live here,' she said slowly. 'But what about us?'

'Ah. . .it's funny that you should mention that,' he murmured. 'As it happens, there is a rather nice place for sale, not too far from London. It has fifty acres of park and woodlands, with a trout stream—surrounding a fifteenth century castle,' he added casually.

'A castle? Do you mean a *real* castle. . .?'

'Umm. . .although it's only been half-restored to its original state, and so there's a lot of work to be done. You'll obviously have to give up your job, now that you're pregnant, and maybe restoring the castle to its former glory would be something to both occupy your time and exercise your brain. Do you think you might be interested?'

Laura's mind was in a whirl as she gazed at him silently for a moment. Of course she was interested—who wouldn't want to live in an ancient castle? And now that she was clearly going to have to give up her job—Ross had made it clear that he wouldn't approve of her returning to work, and especially not when she was expecting a baby—having something to get her teeth into, such as restoring an ancient building, sounded a great idea. As did the suggestion that Liz and Owen might take over the old home. Because, of course, it was Liz's old home as well, and she knew it would mean so much to her cousin to be able to bring up her children in such peaceful surroundings.

'Darling—I think all your ideas are simply wonderful!' she told him happily.

'You're the one who's simply wonderful!' he breathed, his arms enfolding her once more.

Laura yawned, cuddling up closer to him and pressing her cheek into the curve of his shoulder. 'I wonder. . .' she murmured as her eyes closed and she began drifting slowly off to sleep. 'I wonder if we should take out an insurance policy, just in case I might be expecting twins. . .?'

'I can't see the point,' he told sleepily, brushing a stray tendril of her blonde hair from his face. 'We don't have a history of twins in the family—and, in any case, there's a proverb: lightning never strikes twice in the same place, right?'

But he was wrong, as Laura pointed out nine months later when she sat up in bed, proudly holding three-day-old David and James in her arms. She was already getting fed up with the hospital, and couldn't wait to take her twin boys back to the large nursery waiting for them upstairs in the medieval castle that was now the family home.

'If this is what comes of quoting silly old proverbs,' Laura grinned over at her husband, who hadn't recovered from the birth nearly as quickly as she had, 'I think that we'd better be *very* careful what we say in the future!'

As Ross watched her gazing fondly down at the babies, whose heads were already covered with dark hair, and—so Laura had firmly informed him—were carbon copies of their father, he knew that he was an incredibly lucky man. With the wife of his dreams back by his side, and the blessing of two healthy young sons, he now possessed treasures that no amount of money could buy.

Many of his friends had laughingly warned him that he now had 'double trouble'. However, as he gazed lovingly over at his beautiful Laura, gently rocking the tiny babies in her arms, he knew that the true definition of his deep joy and delight lay in the collective noun: a *pride* of lions!

STARGAZING

YOUR STAR SIGN: **LEO (July 24–August 23)**

LEO is the fifth sign of the Zodiac, ruled by the planet Sun and controlled by the element of Fire. These make you proud, exuberant and generous and sometimes arrogant. Your strong sense of power, courage and vanity make you king of the jungle: beware anyone who tries to defy you! But those who can get close to you discover that you're really a pussy cat underneath that hard exterior!

Socially, Leos love fun and games—you possess a lively sense of humour and can roar with laughter as long as the jokes are not made at your expense. At home you are likely to be leader of the pack and enjoy lavishing money to create a warm and secure environment.

Your characteristics in love: Passionate, caring and affectionate, Leos love being in love and will do anything to gain his or her partner's attention and admiration. Nevertheless, once you are adored, you are a very faithful partner and can be quite sensitive, even if you hate to admit it. For the Leo woman, relationships can be quite difficult with you as you insist on getting your own way; being so defiant and demanding, you won't settle for second fiddle. Therefore you are more likely to opt for partners who can fuel your passionate fire and who look after you well.

Signs which are compatible with you: Sagittarius, Aries, Gemini and **Libra**, while **Aquarius, Taurus** and **Scorpio** provide you with a challenge. Partners born under other signs can be compatible, depending on which planets reside in their Houses of Personality and Romance.

What is your star-career? Leos take great pride in their work and enjoy constant recognition for their creative talents. A distinctive regal style, coupled with self-confidence, drives Leos to the top of the career ladder. Positions which need individuality, flair and being in the limelight will appeal to you, such as management, sport, fashion, film work, and teaching.

Your colours and birthstones: Rich, opulent colours such as gold and deep yellows will match your sunny personality. Your birthstones are ruby and amber; they are said to protect the wearer from pains and aches such as headaches. Rubies—also known as a 'a drop

of blood from Mother Earth's heart'—are thought to
have healing powers for diseases of the blood.
Amber—a yellow stone—is said to encourage virility
and fertility.

LEO ASTRO-FACTFILE

Day of the week: Sunday
Countries: Italy and Morocco
Flowers: Daffodil, sunflower, marigold and camomile
Food: Oranges, lemons, fillet steak and pumpkins; Leos enjoy entertaining in great style by planning special celebrations and throwing elaborate dinner parties—so long as they are seated at the head of the table!
Health: Be careful not to go overboard with all that passion and drive in an effort to impress others—you'll have to face up to your mortality sooner or later! Ease up a little and you'll feel much better at the end of the day.

You share your star sign with these famous names:

Whitney Houston	Robert de Niro
Alfred Hitchcock	Yves saint Laurent
Jacqueline Kennedy	Queen Mother
Coco Chanel	Dustin Hoffman
Mick Jagger	George Bernard Shaw
Lucille Ball	Mae West

Next Month's Romances

Each month you can choose from a world of variety in romance with Mills & Boon. Below are the new titles to look out for next month, why not ask either Mills & Boon Reader Service or your Newsagent to reserve you a copy of the titles you want to buy — just tick the titles you would like to order and either post to Reader Service or take it to any Newsagent and ask them to order your books.

Please save me the following titles:	Please tick	√
PAST LOVING	Penny Jordan	
WINTER OF DREAMS	Susan Napier	
KNIGHT TO THE RESCUE	Miranda Lee	
OUT OF NOWHERE	Patricia Wilson	
SECOND CHANCE FOR LOVE	Susanne McCarthy	
MORE THAN A DREAM	Emma Richmond	
REVENGE	Natalie Fox	
YESTERDAY AND FOREVER	Sandra Marton	
NO GENTLEMAN	Kate Walker	
CATALINA'S LOVER	Vanessa Grant	
OLD LOVE, NEW LOVE	Jennifer Taylor	
A FRENCH ENCOUNTER	Cathy Williams	
THE TRESPASSER	Jane Donnelly	
A TEMPTING SHORE	Dana James	
A LOVE TO LAST	Samantha Day	
A PLACE OF WILD HONEY	Ann Charlton	

If you would like to order these books from Mills & Boon Reader Service please send £1.70 per title to: Mills & Boon Reader Service, P.O. Box 236, Croydon, Surrey, CR9 3RU and quote your Subscriber No:...(If applicable) and complete the name and address details below. Alternatively, these books are available from many local Newsagents including W.H.Smith, J.Menzies, Martins and other paperback stockists from 14th August 1992.

Name:..

Address:..

....Post Code:.......................

To Retailer: If you would like to stock M&B books please contact your regular book/magazine wholesaler for details.

You may be mailed with offers from other reputable companies as a result of this application. If you would rather not take advantage of these opportunities please tick box ☐

4 FREE
Romances
and 2 FREE gifts
just for you!

You can enjoy all the
heartwarming emotion of true love for FREE!
Discover the heartbreak and the happiness, the emotion and
the tenderness of the modern relationships in
Mills & Boon Romances.

We'll send you 4 captivating Romances as a special offer from
Mills & Boon Reader Service, along with the chance to have
6 Romances delivered to your door each month.

Claim your FREE books and gifts overleaf...

An irresistible offer from Mills & Boon

Here's a personal invitation from Mills & Boon Reader Service, to become a regular reader of Romances. To welcome you, we'd like you to have 4 books, a CUDDLY TEDDY and a special MYSTERY GIFT absolutely FREE.

Then you could look forward each month to receiving 6 brand new Romances, delivered to your door, postage and packing free! Plus our free Newsletter featuring author news, competitions, special offers and much more.

This invitation comes with no strings attached. You may cancel or suspend your subscription at any time, and still keep your free books and gifts.

It's so easy. Send no money now. Simply fill in the coupon below and post it to - **Reader Service, FREEPOST, PO Box 236, Croydon, Surrey CR9 9EL.**

NO STAMP REQUIRED

Free Books Coupon

Yes! Please rush me 4 free Romances and 2 free gifts! Please also reserve me a Reader Service subscription. If I decide to subscribe I can look forward to receiving 6 brand new Romances each month for just £10.20, postage and packing free. If I choose not to subscribe I shall write to you within 10 days - I can keep the books and gifts whatever I decide. I may cancel or suspend my subscription at any time. I am over 18 years of age.

Ms/Mrs/Miss/Mr_____ EP31R

Address _____

_____

Postcode_____Signature _____